ABOUT THE AUTHOR

Lorraine Johnson is a writer, researcher and editor who lives and works in Toronto. She was born in Stratford, Ontario, and raised in Galt. After graduating from the University of Toronto, she worked in magazine and book publishing, most recently as an editor at Penguin Books. She credits her father (an inveterate recycler) with instilling environmental concerns in her life at an early age and for encouraging her to translate concerns into action. She is a member of many environmental groups.

GREEN FUTURE

HOW TO MAKE A WORLD OF DIFFERENCE

Lorraine Johnson

Foreword by Friends of the Earth

Penguin Books

PENGUIN BOOKS
Published by the Penguin Group
Penguin Books Canada Ltd, 2801 John Street, Markham, Ontario L3R 1B4
Penguin Books Ltd, 27 Wrights Lane, London W8 5TZ, England
Viking Penguin Inc., 40 West 23rd Street, New York, New York, 10010, USA
Penguin Books Australia Ltd, Ringwood, Victoria, Australia
Penguin Books (NZ) Ltd, 182-190 Wairau Road, Auckland 10, New Zealand

Penguin Books Ltd, Registered Offices: Harmondsworth, Middlesex, England

First published by Penguin Books, 1990
10 9 8 7 6 5 4 3 2 1

DESIGN: Brant Cowie / ArtPlus Limited
PAGE MAKE UP: Heather Brunton / ArtPlus Limited
TYPE OUTPUT: TypeLine Express Limited
Manufactured in Canada on recycled acid free paper ♾

Canadian Cataloguing in Publication Data
Johnson, Lorraine, 1960-
    Green future

ISBN   0-14-012301-6

1. Environmental protection.   2. Pollution.   3. Human ecology.
4. Recycling (Waste, etc.).   I. Title

TD170.2.J63 1990   363.7   C89-095239-6

For my father, my brothers—
Keith and Ross—
and for Andrew,
with much love and many thanks.

Acknowledgements

This book would not have been possible without the generous assistance of many people. I offer my sincere thanks to John Barker, Noona Barlow, Nick Bibikov, Joe Black, Michael Bloomfield, Cecelia Burke-Lawless, Gail and Jy Chiperzac, Terry Churchill, Pat Cooper, Lois Corbett, Jill Courtemanche, Tania Craan, Jill Dunkley, Gail Fisher-Taylor, Rick Forsyth, Susan Glover, Mary Granskou, Laurie Henderson, Alma Johnson, Shirley Langer, Sheila McCrindle, Tom Moull, Mike Nickerson, Carolyn O'Neill, Gordon Perks, Kerri Sakamoto, Pierre Sassone, Jeremy Stiles, Celia and Digby Viets, Burns Wattie, Tim Weatherill, and the Tuesday night Pilot group.

For their valuable guidance and help with the manuscript, I would like to thank the following people who reviewed specific chapters: Adele Hurley ("Acid Rain"), Robert Hornung and Andrea Prazmowski ("Losing the Ozone Layer"), Joyce McLean ("Water"), Peggy Hallward ("Vanishing Forests"), John Hanson ("Garbage" and "Toxic Wastes and Hazardous Substances"), Rod McRae ("Agriculture"), Ken Cox and Vicky Husband ("Wilderness"), David Rousseau (indoor air quality), Mike Nickerson ("Green Consumer"). Kristina Marie Guiguet provided valuable research assistance for which I am grateful. Debbie Viets read the manuscript and offered insightful and useful editorial suggestions. Julia Langer wrote the Foreword, and I thank her for Friends of the Earth's support and encouragement. Iris Skeoch, Executive Editor at Penguin Books, has been a good friend, guide and editor from the project's beginning; her comments were always inspiring. Thanks to Elynor Kagan for doing the copy editing, Kathryn Dean for the production editing, Cy Strom for proofreading, Brant Cowie for the text design, Heather Brunton for the typesetting and Catherine Marjoribanks for doing the final check. Many thanks to everyone at Penguin for their enthusiasm above and beyond the call of duty; they made the whole process a delight and I am very much indebted to them.

A world of thanks to Selby, Keith and Ross Johnson for being constant sources of inspiration and delight.

Contents

GREEN FUTURE

HOW TO MAKE A WORLD OF DIFFERENCE

Foreword

by Julia Langer
Executive Director, Friends of the Earth

The number of calls and letters that come to the Friends of the Earth office has grown astronomically over the past few years. If I could summarize what people are saying, it would be: "I know the world is going to hell in a handbasket, but what can I do about it?" Obviously Lorraine Johnson has heard your questions too. *Green Future* is a book so clearly needed I can only wonder why it took so long for someone to write it. The sad thing is we need it badly. The truth is we need it urgently.

We have been living in a state of ignorance about the vital relationship between the natural world and ourselves. Sure, some of us were disturbed by the fouling of beautiful lakes and rivers, upset by pictures of animals nearing extinction, annoyed that certain companies were exceeding pollution guidelines. Some were sorry that forests were being cut down so fast, and puzzled by the appearance of a hole in the ozone layer. But, in the past, pollution was neither perceived nor treated as a problem. People thought that, since pollution "disappeared" into the air and water, it wasn't dangerous. The "environment" was seen as the domain of bird watchers and other "nature lovers."

As individuals and as a society, we have become alienated from nature. Perhaps we have forgotten that nature is more than a beautiful view, a Sunday drive, an occasional wilderness holiday. Nature has been regarded as a wholesome retreat from which we return refreshed to our sinful urban habits, or something to be manipulated and used to satisfy our ideas of progress and development.

Only recently, when environmental problems have come knocking on our own doors and showing up on our daily menu of news, have we started realizing that the planet is in rough shape. Still, most of us haven't made the connection between what we see and read about and our own daily lives. Humans — us, all of us — are only part of the natural chain of life, yet we have tried to divide and conquer the other links. It is time to realize that the key to our survival on planet earth is to preserve and protect planet earth.

Environmental protection is about preservation of everything natural, since everything in nature performs a vital function for the mutual benefit of all. Each small part of the ecosystem is dependent on the whole for its continued existence. Where will we be without clean water, fresh air, and beautiful vistas? More fundamentally, why should we humans be determining the fate of birds, trees, rivers or microscopic ocean life to serve our own lifestyles?

Quite suddenly, it seems the whole world has been (appropriately) jolted by the backlash of the long-abused global environment. The impact of human activities upon natural systems is taking its toll — the record of chemical spills, nuclear accidents, water contamination, exponentially growing population, loss of species, deforestation is mounting. These symptoms of an overused, abused, and taken-for-granted planet can no longer be ignored.

Canadians have tended to trust that there are laws that would protect us, wildlife, rivers, lakes and the air. In fact, there are few laws that guarantee or protect the rights of all citizens to clean air, water and soil. Activity that damages the environment is not necessarily against the law in Canada, even though there have been some improvements over the years in reaction to tighter standards, new technologies, and public opinion.

While spewing effluent pipes and black, belching smokestacks are now the exception rather than the rule, environmental degradation continues in another, potentially more damaging mode. Unsustainable exploitation of trees, soil, minerals and water is the beast that must be confronted in the coming decade. The planet is being defaced, mined, logged, paved, doused with chemicals, heated up, and turned into products. It is being used as a dumping ground at a faster and faster pace as human numbers grow and grow and expectations of the western lifestyle spread and spread. How much more can it take? Not much.

But things are changing. There is a growing awareness that our fate is not separate from the fate of the ecosystem; we are seeing and feeling our lives threatened by pollution previously felt to be "out there," far beyond our own backyards.

The "greening" of politics worldwide would seem to indicate that governments are accepting the obligation to restore and protect the environment so as to preserve our natural heritage. But don't hold your breath. To date, we have yet to see the Canadian government take real action to guarantee substantial reduction of pollution and environmental degradation or changes to the basic policy of encouraging resource exploitation. What we have is a case of green rhetoric.

It all comes back to the basic question: What must be done? Starting now, and as many times as it takes, we must indicate to our lagging government, industries and institutions that protection of the environment is our first priority. Let's point fingers, even if they point right back to us. Let's not be blackmailed into accepting environmentally degrading trade-offs in order to protect jobs that are contributing to environmental destruction: there is too much to lose and there are sounder ways for an economy and society to function. The fact of the matter is that unlimited economic growth and consumption are not sustainable on this relatively small, fragile planet with finite resources.

Although the media often take a "here today, gone tomorrow" approach to environmental problems, or see them only as issues of contention among interest groups, media coverage of environmental issues is now omnipresent and growing in detail. Imagine *Time* magazine opting for "Planet of the Year" instead of the usual public figure! Something must be getting through. Media coverage has also taught everyone the names and locations of the problems. Who can forget Bhopal, Three Mile Island and Chernobyl, the burning of the Amazon rainforest, the poisoning of the Rhine, the *Exxon Valdez*? Who can escape the knowledge that, for every one of the headlines, other major and minor environmental disasters occur out of the limelight?

A trickle of information that goes beyond the thirty-second clip has begun to appear. It is helping to focus attention on the deepening nature of the environmental crisis, daring to point fingers and propose solutions. With limited resources, environmental organizations have published pamphlets, posters and booklets. For example, Friends of the Earth has factsheets and books on how to clean our homes without toxic chemicals and get our lawns and gardens off drugs. The media are publishing and broadcasting feature stories on the environment, even though these are often slim on concrete suggestions for action. Government publications abound, even though they sit unread on office racks.

And corporations are getting into the environment act: they read the polls and recognize that environmental protection is a priority for their customers. Companies are advertising "environmentally friendly" products. However, consumers must beware — "environmentally friendly" is a hard label to live up to. Besides, it is overconsumption and wrongheaded consumption that has led us into this environmental mess and simply switching brands is not the way out of it.

Canadians have indicated to the pollsters that they are willing to pay more and do more to help protect the environment. What we need is an explanation of how our very lifestyles and social values nourish the roots of environmental degradation, and how they can be changed.

Green Future does deal with the full spectrum of environmental problems. It rightfully places a share of the burden of responsibility upon each of us, but it's not depressing. By providing us with specific ways to start protecting the environment, the author dispels our feelings of helplessness and hopelessness. This guide helps translate will into action, if your will is to start treading more lightly on the earth.

The need and desire to protect ourselves and our children and their children is universal and elemental. First start with the understanding that our future is linked with the planet's. Then, the information between these two covers will empower you to do all you can to build a green future.

I am confident that together we can protect the earth for tomorrow.

Never doubt that a small group of thoughtful, committed citizens can change the world. Indeed it's the only thing that ever has.
— Margaret Mead

Julia Langer
Executive Director, Friends of the Earth
Summer, 1989

PART I

Understanding the Issues: The Key to Action

"At the rate we are going, the world will come to an end. Oceans and rivers will one day be sterile, the land will lose all productivity, city air will be stifling and life itself will be a privilege." Who is uttering this gloomy prediction of a devastated and radically altered world? Is this vision of the future the product of an overactive and alarmist imagination?

These words were spoken in June 1989 by the federal Minister of the Environment, Lucien Bouchard. There is plenty of evidence to support his scenario: the world's deserts are growing at an annual rate of 6 million hectares (that's equal to one Nova Scotia turned to sand and dust every year); 14 hectares of forest are cut down worldwide every minute; the composition of the atmosphere has been changed by human activity in just a few decades; the ozone layer is being destroyed; 24 billion tonnes of productive topsoil are lost worldwide every year; and at least one species is lost forever every hour of every day.

The future that Bouchard sees is inevitable *if we continue with our destructive practices*. However, it is not the future that has to be. We have a choice. Quite simply, either we can continue to degrade the environment without regard for the land, air, water and millions of species with which we share the planet *or* we can say that it's time to end this madness *now*. In fact, is there really a choice, after all? Does species extinction, a polluted environment and the poisoning of the human race stand up as an option that anyone would consciously choose?

Yet this is exactly the course we are taking. There isn't a place left on earth that is untouched by contamination caused by human activity. How did we get to this point and how are we going to turn the situation around?

The Decade of Decision

We need everyone's heart, everyone's mind. We need the brainpower of every human being on this planet.
— Ron Smith, EDEN Foundation

In most discussions and media reports, the word that usually follows *environmental* is *problem*. We tend to associate the environment with bad news, disasters we'd rather ignore, hopeless situations that make us feel powerless. The result: we remove ourselves, hoping that these problems won't touch our daily lives. But they are not self-contained problems that can be dissociated from the larger system of inter-relationships or from cause and effect. In fact, most problems are really symptoms, the causes of which can be found in human activity — our use of fossil fuels, our efforts to control nature, our overconsumption of manufactured goods, our growing population. In short, we have developed a lifestyle that is propped up by environmental destruction. We have lived for short-term goals at the expense of long-term sustainability.

As more and more people become aware of the destructive course we are on, as environmental issues enter daily news reports, it becomes more and more difficult to ignore the signs of environmental degradation. The evidence, which has always been with us and which enlightened scientists, activists and even some policymakers have been pointing out for years, is brought into public focus. The extended heat wave and drought of the summer of 1988 was not simply a temporary (and, to farmers, economically disastrous) problem; rather it was treated as a sign of the atmospheric chaos caused by the greenhouse effect. As more environmental problems are recognized for what they are — symptoms of destructive human activity — and as the manifestations provide daily evidence for all individuals to see, then perhaps we will begin to make the massive shifts, both in actions and in attitudes, that are necessary to change the catastrophic path we are on.

Ecosystem versus Egosystem

Unless we change our direction, we are likely to end up where we are headed.
— Chinese proverb

We share this planet with at least five million species. We are just one. The egosystem approach (the attitude that allows us, as just one species, to continue destroying an estimated 1 to 24 species every day) will have to be replaced with a recognition that all living things are interconnected.

Even in purely human terms, every social system we have created — including our economic system — depends on the environment. If we destroy the planet, all other systems will collapse along with it. And if we don't change our notion of progress, if we continue to measure it in terms of blind growth, then we will destroy the very environment that makes our "progress" possible.

Consider a group of people poised at the edge of a cliff. Their idea of progress dictates that they keep moving forward. There is no doubt that we are at the edge. We can either continue forward or take at least one step backwards and ask how we arrived at the edge of the cliff in the first place.

Acid Rain:
And Snow, and Fog,
and Hail, and...

A century ago, coal miners would carry a canary into a mine to monitor the air quality of their environment. If the level of explosive and toxic methane gas rose, the canary would die. If the canary's song ceased, the miners knew it was time to get out. Perhaps the trout and salmon in acid lakes are serving this function in the north woods. The fish are vanishing: the canary falls silent.

— JON LUOMA, *TROUBLED SKIES, TROUBLED WATERS*

THE PROBLEM:

Acid rain, caused by pollutants released into the atmosphere, is killing forests, lakes and animals, damaging buildings and structures, and harming human health.

THE SOLUTION:

Reduce emissions of pollutants into the atmosphere.

In *Troubled Skies, Troubled Waters* Jon Luoma points out that "during a typical, moderate rain shower, some five million drops of water will fall on each acre of land per second, with a force of 2.3 pounds per square inch per drop." If the rain in that shower has the acidity of vinegar, imagine what each of those five million drops does to soil, plants, lakes, animals, buildings and humans. In many parts of Canada, "gentle" or "soft" rain has been replaced with acid rain.

DEFINITION

Acid precipitation or deposition — which includes rain, snow, fog, sleet, hail, dew, dust and particles — is the result of sulphur dioxide (SO_2) and oxides of nitrogen (NO_x) emissions into the air. Once in the atmosphere, these contaminants react with moisture, sunlight, oxygen and other gases to create sulphuric and nitric acids, which fall on the earth as acid precipitation or dry acidic particles.

Acidity is measured using the pH scale, which goes from 0 to 14. The lower the number, the more acidic the solution. Because the scale is logarithmic, a measurement of pH3 is 10 times more acidic than pH4, and 100 times more acidic than pH5. "Clean" or "pure" rain has a pH of 5.6; rain with a pH measurement lower than this is acid rain.

The rain that falls on Canada has, on average, a pH of somewhere between 4 and 4.5. Acid rain is now the norm in eastern Canada. And this measurement is just the average. The rain falling on eastern Canada is often up to 50 times more acidic. Rain over most of southern Ontario has an annual mean acidity of 4.2 — as acidic as a tomato.

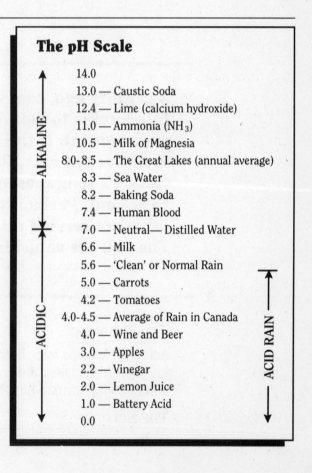

The pH Scale

ALKALINE

14.0
13.0 — Caustic Soda
12.4 — Lime (calcium hydroxide)
11.0 — Ammonia (NH_3)
10.5 — Milk of Magnesia
8.0-8.5 — The Great Lakes (annual average)
8.3 — Sea Water
8.2 — Baking Soda
7.4 — Human Blood
7.0 — Neutral— Distilled Water
6.6 — Milk
5.6 — 'Clean' or Normal Rain
5.0 — Carrots
4.2 — Tomatoes
4.0-4.5 — Average of Rain in Canada
4.0 — Wine and Beer
3.0 — Apples
2.2 — Vinegar
2.0 — Lemon Juice
1.0 — Battery Acid
0.0

ACIDIC

ACID RAIN

CAUSES

The major sources of sulphur dioxide emissions are ore smelters and coal-burning power stations. Most of Canadian SO_2 comes from just a handful of sources. The major SO_2 emissions in Ontario, for example, are from Inco, Falconbridge, Algoma Steel and Ontario Hydro. In Quebec, Noranda is a major contributor of SO_2.

Emissions of nitrogen oxides come mainly from vehicle exhaust and power plants. Estimates vary but the breakdown of NO_x emissions in North America is roughly 27% from residential and commercial sources (fuel combustion for heating), 40% from vehicle exhaust (including cars, trucks, trains and planes), and 33% from power plants.

Sulphur dioxide and nitrogen oxides can travel long distances in the atmosphere, hence acid rain may fall hundreds of kilometres away from the pollution source. Officials at Environment Canada estimate that more than half of the acid deposition in eastern Canada originates from U.S. emissions. On the other hand, from 10 to 25% of the acid rain in some parts of the northeastern United States is of Canadian origin.

EFFECTS

The impact of acid rain on soil and water depends on two factors: the amount of acid deposition (either in wet or dry form) and the sensitivity of the area's soil, vegetation or water to acidification.

The environmental effects of acid rain are generally divided into the following categories: aquatic, terrestrial, material and human health. Relatively few studies have been done on the health effects on animals other than fish.

Aquatic Effects

Imagine a crystal clear, blue-green lake. You can see right to the bottom, where there is a perfect leaf resting on the sand. It hasn't decomposed. The lake is still and beautiful. It is also dead. There are no fish, no birds, no amphibians, no mammals.

There are at least 14,000 biologically dead, acidified lakes in Canada. Approximately 150,000 more are being damaged. More than 350,000 are considered vulnerable or sensitive, which means that eventually they will die if they continue to receive high levels of acid rain.

Scientists' ability to predict the length of time it takes a lake to acidify is still limited at this stage. However, they do know that the speed depends on the lake's ability to buffer or neutralize the acid. If, for example, the surrounding rocks and soil are alkaline limestone, the acid will be neutralized to a degree. However, 46% (4,000,000 km^2) of all the land in Canada contains aquatic ecosystems that are highly sensitive to acid rain. Another 21% (1,800,000 km^2) is moderately sensitive. Only 23% (2,000,000 km^2) is generally considered not sensitive to acid rain.

An aquatic ecosystem is adversely affected if the pH of the water is below 6. At pH 5.5, there are fewer species in the lake, and those remaining have trouble surviving. Few fish can reproduce if the pH of the lake is below 5. Fish are threatened not only by the increased acidity of their environment, but also by the toxic heavy metals such as lead, mercury and aluminum that leach into the water from the surrounding rocks and soil. The solubility of metals increases under acidic conditions. Therefore, the more acidic the water, the more these metals are activated in the soil, enter the water and build up in the fish. If the fish is eaten by a bird, the poisons are passed up the food chain.

As increasing acidity kills organism after organism, the whole aquatic ecosystem is threatened. If the pH of the water drops below 4.5, most fish and aquatic life will die. After the fish, snails, bullfrogs, crawfish and most other lifeforms have disappeared, only highly resistant species like slimy filamentous algae will be alive in the lake.

Outlook for the Eastern Provinces

Most of the attention to acid rain has been focussed on the damage being done to the provinces east of Manitoba and the areas south of James Bay. This focus is warranted for three main reasons: most of the industrial activity that produces SO_2 and NO_x in both the United States and Canada occurs in the central and eastern regions; most of the acid-rain producing pollutants that are transported by air land as acid deposition in the eastern provinces; and, in many eastern areas, the soils and aquatic systems do not have the natural buffering capacity to neutralize the acid.

There are an estimated 700,000 lakes in eastern Canada. More than half are considered sensitive to acid rain. At least 148,000 have a pH below 6, the level at which adverse biological effects occur.

Newfoundland and Labrador: An estimated 30% of the lakes have a pH below 6. At least 1.8% are acidified, and, of the lakes studied, over 95% are considered to be extremely sensitive or vulnerable to acid deposition.

Nova Scotia: Over 73% of the lakes in Nova Scotia have a pH below 6. Approximately 47% are acidified. Scientists estimate that 49% of salmon production in the southern upland rivers has been lost because of acidification. In the whole province over 33% of salmon production has been lost.

New Brunswick: An estimated 35% of lakes have a pH below 6. Over 15% are acidified. Large sportfishing areas in the province are considered sensitive to acid deposition.

Quebec: Over 16% of the lakes are estimated to have a pH below 6. At least 1.4% are acidified. Brook trout have disappeared from many lakes in the Charlevoix region. In the Outaouais area, 63% of lakes studied had a pH of 6.0 or less, and 23% were acidified.

Ontario: Over 22% of lakes are estimated to have a pH below 6. Approximately 1.6% are acidified. (The Ontario Ministry of the Environment, however, estimates that a much higher 5.2% are acidified. For bleak reading, see the ministry's publication "Acid Sensitivity of Lakes in Ontario," which lists acidified lakes by name.) Approximately 36,000 lakes are sensitive to acid rain.

Source: Department of Fisheries and Oceans, *Acid Rain: Time is Running Out*

Outlook for the Western Provinces

The environment ministries in the western provinces have coordinated their acid rain monitoring and research programs under the Long-Range Transport of Air Pollutants in Western and Northern Canada program. The program's aim is to evaluate the impact that acidic deposition is having in the west and north, and to ensure that it does not become a significant problem, as it has in the east.

Northwest Territories: Lakes to the east of the Precambrian Shield are highly sensitive to acid deposition.

British Columbia: In coastal and mountainous areas of northern British Columbia and the West Kootenay region, the soil is highly sensitive to acid deposition. Lakes within approximately 250 km of the west coast, on Vancouver Island and the Queen Charlotte Islands, are considered of high or moderate sensitivity.

Alberta: Lakes in the Birch Mountains area of the Fort McMurray region and most lakes in the Caribou Mountain region are considered moderately to highly sensitive to acid deposition. Sensitive lakes are also found in the Jasper National Park region.

Saskatchewan: Lakes within the Precambrian Shield region are highly sensitive to acid deposition, although the lakes along the southern boundary of the Shield are moderately sensitive.

Manitoba: The area east of Lake Winnipeg is moderately sensitive to acidic input, while the northern region is considered highly sensitive.

Source: B.C. Ministry of Environment and Parks, *Acid Rain in British Columbia*; Coordinating Committee on Surface Waters for Western and Northern LRTAP Technical Committee, *Sensitivity of Western and Northern Canada Surface Waters to Acidic Inputs*

Terrestrial Effects

Acid rain also affects the pH of soil and, therefore, the health of anything that grows. The more acidic the soil, the easier it is for nutrients necessary for growth, such as potassium, to be leached out of the soil and washed away before they are absorbed by plants. At the same time, toxic metals such as aluminum and mercury are leached out of the acidic soil. Thus, not only do plants lose essential nutrients, they also absorb harmful metals.

While damage occurs in the soil below, plants are also assaulted by acidic deposition landing directly on their leaves and needles, injuring protective barks and leaf surfaces. As plants become more damaged, they are more susceptible to infestation by pests and fungi.

How to Recognize Signs of Tree Damage from Acid Rain

• Branches at the top of the tree are bare.
• Leaves are sparse on the branches.
• Remaining leaves are discoloured.
• Leaves begin changing their colours earlier than autumn.

"If trees could make sounds, their collective screams around the world would be deafening." — David Suzuki, *Globe and Mail*

In eastern Canada 84% of the most productive agricultural lands receive high levels of acid deposition annually. Environment Canada estimates the value of the damage at $1 billion every year. Approximately 55% of eastern Canada's forests, which generate $14 billion worth of forest products a year, receive high levels of acid rain. In some parts of Ontario and Quebec, growth rates of pine, spruce and fir have more than halved.

The $60 million a year maple syrup industry in Quebec has already experienced dramatic decreases in productivity. More than 80% of the sugar bushes in the province have been affected by acid rain. Current predictions suggest that all of Quebec's sugar bushes will be unproductive within a decade. Over 60% of maple sugar bush owners surveyed in New Brunswick in 1985 reported deterioration of their trees.

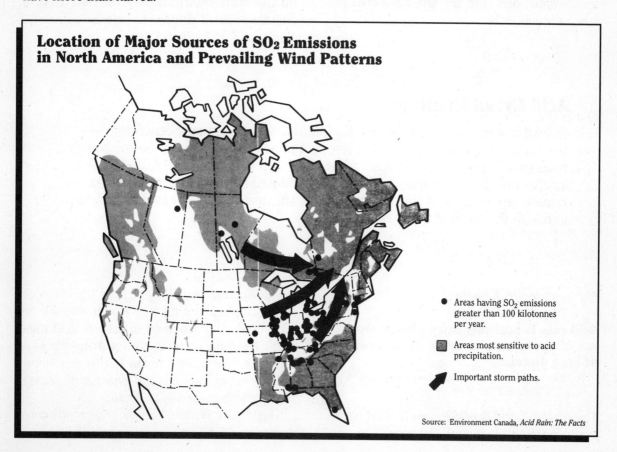

Location of Major Sources of SO₂ Emissions in North America and Prevailing Wind Patterns

- Areas having SO_2 emissions greater than 100 kilotonnes per year.

- Areas most sensitive to acid precipitation.

- Important storm paths.

Source: Environment Canada, *Acid Rain: The Facts*

Effects on Materials

As you can see from the effect of a dripping tap on an enamelled sink, water corrodes material over time. With acid rain, the natural corrosion and deterioration of materials is speeded up. Metals, plastics, paints, brick, stone, concrete — all are affected. Of course, these materials weaken naturally but many are particularly damaged by acid rain. Limestone, marble, iron, steel, copper and zinc are just a few that are especially vulnerable.

Next time you curse salty roads in winter for rusting your car, consider that half of the automobile corrosion in Canada may be caused by acid rain. The House of Commons sub-committee on acid rain estimated that acid rain causes a staggering $285 million damage to building materials per year. Others set a much higher figure. According to Martin Weaver, who for more than a decade has studied the effects of acid rain on the built environment, the 1981 cost of pollution-related damage to exterior paintwork alone was $ 0.83 billion.

Acid Green Rooftops

At least one part of the Parliament Buildings in Ottawa actually benefitted — aesthetically, at least — from corrosive acid rain. The green patina on the copper roofs used to take about ten years to develop, with the "help" of polluted air. After a paper mill directly across the Ottawa River closed in 1972, the Public Works Department found that they had to patinate the new parts of the roof artificially to match the green of the old copper.

Human Health Effects

Acid rain is probably third after active smoking and passive smoking as a cause of lung disease.
— Dr. Philip Landrigan, Mount Sinai School of Medicine, New York City, *Globe and Mail*, February 5, 1987

The effects of acid deposition on human health are being studied, though the results are debated. Environment Canada calls the evidence "inconclusive," noting that it is impossible to attribute health problems directly to acid rain. While the same could be said of many environmental contaminant/human health equations, there is mounting statistical evidence of adverse health effects caused by acid rain.

Health and Welfare Canada is currently conducting a $6 million joint study with Harvard

University to measure the lung capacity of 15,000 children in six Canadian and eighteen American cities. The study follows a 1986 investigation which found that children living in Canadian areas of high acid rain had, on average, lung capacity reduced by 2%. These children also had a higher incidence of breathing problems such as dust allergies, stuffy noses and coughs with phlegm.

Dr. David Bates, Professor Emeritus of Medicine at the University of British Columbia, studied eight years of hospital records and air pollution readings in southern Ontario. He found that hospital admissions for respiratory problems doubled during periods of high ozone levels and sulphate pollution. Such a statistical correlation is not conclusive, but it certainly is suggestive.

Health specialists have also speculated that an increase in acidity of drinking water drawn from sources affected by acid rain would have serious public health consequences. Through the same process described in the sections on aquatic and terrestrial effects, heavy metals are leached from surrounding pipes or surrounding soil by acidic water. In cities where lead pipes are used, or where lead solder joins the pipes, heavy metals could leach into the water supply if the pH of the water were not adjusted before distribution. The main source of drinking water in Atlantic Canada — groundwater — is especially at risk from heavy metal contamination because the soil does not buffer or neutralize acid rain.

While scientists debate the results of these studies and some people dismiss the evidence as speculative, there is no doubt that sulphur dioxide and nitrogen oxides in high concentrations are damaging to human health. According to Environment Canada, more than 80% of Canadians live in areas where acidic deposition is high.

Not only do nitrogen oxides contribute to acid rain, they also lead to the formation of ozone which, at ground level, is a serious pollutant. Recent U.S. studies reveal that ground-level ozone pollution is causing extensive and possibly irreversible lung injury. Top environmental scientists have found that laboratory animals exposed to the levels of ozone pollution found in U.S. cities suffered lung lesions as severe as those found in smokers. In addition, children breathing low levels of ozone suffered lung impairment and lost as much as 42% of their lung function for days or weeks.

SOLUTIONS

Approximately 80% of our air pollution stems from hydrocarbons released by vegetation, so let's not go overboard in setting and enforcing tough emission standards from man-made sources.
— Ronald Reagan, September 1980, quoted by David Israelson in
  Toronto Star, April 6, 1987

Despite Ronald Reagan's astonishing attempt to blame trees, acid rain is a problem created by human activity and it is already having a significant effect on our resource-based economy. Agriculture, forestry, tourism and fishing are the major industries at risk. At present, Environment Canada estimates that acid rain causes $1 billion worth of damage in eastern Canada every year — that's over 3% of the 1989 federal deficit. Unless emissions of sulphur dioxide and nitrogen oxides are dramatically reduced in both the United States and Canada, this figure will certainly continue to rise.

North American industries (mainly coal-burning power plants and ore smelters) and automobiles dump over 50 million tonnes of SO_2 and NO_x into the air every year. Although Canada produces fewer SO_2 emissions than the United States, Canadian *per capita* emissions exceed those of the U.S.

The technology needed to clean up emissions substantially at their sources already exists. Low sulphur coal (produced, for example, in western Canada) could be immediately introduced in coal-burning power plants;

scrubbers could be installed in power plants to reduce the sulphur content of emissions; vehicles with better pollution control could be engineered. The impediments to such controls are economic and political. The federal and provincial governments are, however, taking action.

In an effort to reduce emissions, Environment Canada launched a major acid rain control program in 1985. The goal is to reduce total SO_2 emissions from the Saskatchewan-Manitoba border eastward to 2.3 million tonnes a year by 1994. This represents a 50% reduction from 1980 levels.

The federal government is not specifying how industries are required to reach the reduction goals. However, each province has set emission standards and major SO_2 producers are reporting to respective governments on their reduction plans.

The federal government also set standards for NO_x emissions that came into effect in 1987 for cars and 1988 for heavy trucks and buses. However, because the number of automobiles in use is rising, these regulations will keep NO_x emissions at their current level only until the mid-1990s.

Half of the acid rain that falls on Canada is caused by U.S. pollution; therefore, any efforts to "clean up" have to be directed to the American government and industries. Even if Canada eliminated *all* SO_2 emissions, some sensitive lakes in eastern Canada would continue to die as a result of acidification from U.S. sources.

Sources of Eastern Canadian SO$_2$ Emissions in 1980: 4.6 million tonnes in total — approximately one-fifth of a tonne per Canadian

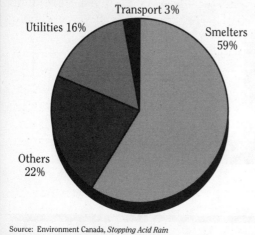

Transport 3%

Utilities 16%

Smelters 59%

Others 22%

Source: Environment Canada, *Stopping Acid Rain*

Sources of Eastern Canadian NO$_x$ Emissions in 1980: 1.7 million tonnes in total — approximately one-fourteenth of a tonne per Canadian

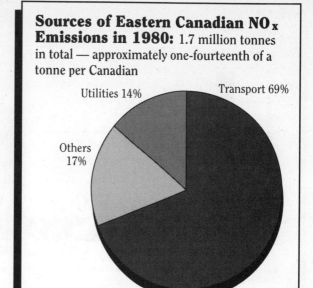

Utilities 14%

Transport 69%

Others 17%

Source: Environment Canada, *Stopping Acid Rain*

Level of Canadian SO$_2$ Emissions

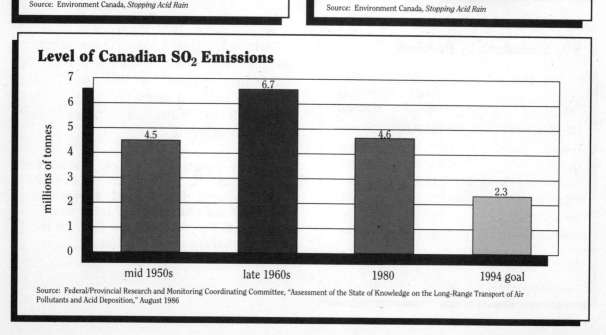

Source: Federal/Provincial Research and Monitoring Coordinating Committee, "Assessment of the State of Knowledge on the Long-Range Transport of Air Pollutants and Acid Deposition," August 1986

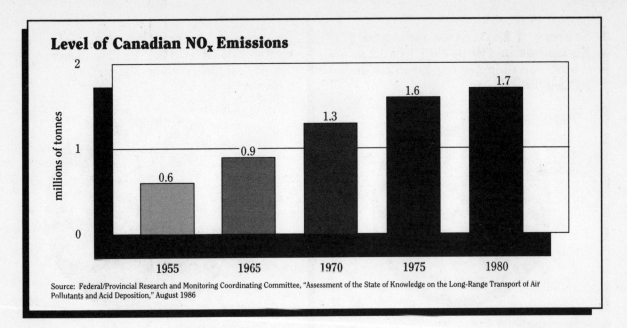

Level of Canadian NO$_x$ Emissions

(millions of tonnes)

Year	millions of tonnes
1955	0.6
1965	0.9
1970	1.3
1975	1.6
1980	1.7

Source: Federal/Provincial Research and Monitoring Coordinating Committee, "Assessment of the State of Knowledge on the Long-Range Transport of Air Pollutants and Acid Deposition," August 1986

SO$_2$ Emissions by Province

	1980 Levels (tonnes)	1994 Objectives (tonnes)
Manitoba	738,000	550,000
Ontario	2,194,000	885,000
Quebec	1,085,000	600,000
New Brunswick	215,000	185,000
Prince Edward Island	6,000	5,000
Nova Scotia	219,000	204,000
Newfoundland	59,000	45,000
Total	4,516,000	2,474,000

Source: Environment Canada, *Stopping Acid Rain*

As long ago as 1980, the U.S. and Canadian governments signed a Memorandum of Intent to limit transboundary air pollution. But little has actually been done. In 1986, the U.S. attitude was summed up by Lee Thomas, then administrator of the U.S. Environmental Protection Agency (E.P.A.):

Acid rain is a serious problem, but it's not an emergency.... At this time the damage caused by acid rain is mostly theoretical. Theoretical damage should leave us on our guard, but it should not force us to take premature control actions.

EPA Journal, June/July, 1986

However, the outlook for the future is more positive. William Reilly, the new head of the E.P.A., has publicly stated that acid rain control will be a priority for the Bush administration; and in 1989, the U.S. Congress and the White House began to negotiate clean-air legislation. In the summer of 1989, President Bush expressed willingness to consider signing a bilateral acid rain accord with Canada.

"The pollution issue came up a second time when [Mrs. Bush and Mrs. Mulroney] visited the National Gallery.

"Mrs. Bush looked at A. Y. Jackson's *November* and Tom Thomson's *Jack Pine*, two of the country's better known northern landscapes and proclaimed, 'They're beautiful.'

"'Did you know those lakes are dying?' asked a reporter. Either not hearing the question or ignoring it, Mrs. Bush repeated, 'They're beautiful' and kept moving."

— *Globe and Mail*

A Long Time Coming

1661-62: Two British investigators, John Evelyn and John Graunt, publish separate studies that discuss the negative effects of industrial emissions on plants and humans.

1872: An English scientist, Robert Angus Smith, creates the term "acid rain" in the book *Air and Rain: The Beginnings of a Chemical Climatology*.

1972: Two Canadian scientists, R.J. Beamish and H.H. Harvey, find that fish populations have declined as a result of the acidification of Canadian lakes.

Source: Ellis B. Cowling in *Environmental Science and Technology*, Vol. 16, No. 2; *EPA Journal*, June/July, 1986

While governments continue to "study the problem," negotiate and hammer out an agreement, an innovative project has been launched by a Quebec group, L'Association québécoise de lutte contre les pluies acides (AQLPA). By "twinning" towns and cities in Quebec with communities in the United States, the group hopes to mobilize support from their American neighbours to reduce acid rain.

The major non-government group fighting acid rain, the Canadian Coalition on Acid Rain, also directs many of its lobbying efforts to the U.S. government and people. In one graphic campaign, the coalition — with help from the Federation of Ontario Cottagers' Associations — sent samples of maple syrup packed in wood from Quebec's pollution-damaged trees to all members of the U.S. House of Representatives and Senate. The maple syrup containers were only half full.

WHAT CAN I DO?

- Emissions of sulphur dioxide and nitrogen oxides can be controlled by installing pollution control technologies, reducing the sulphur content of coal and reducing the use of fossil fuels. Most individuals don't have direct control over the first two. However, in the area of reducing use of fossil fuels, each person can make a difference.

  Quite simply, if we want to reduce the level of sulphur dioxide and nitrogen oxides emissions, we have to use less energy (particularly non-renewable fossil fuels) and use energy more efficiently. Conservation of energy is one acid rain control that doesn't cost money and is available to each and every one of us right now. Every day.

  For details on how to reduce your energy needs and how to use energy more efficiently, see Chapter 12, "Energy: Turning On Efficiency," Chapter 13, "Energy Conservation in the Home," and Chapter 15, "Transportation."

- Recycling materials is another way to reduce energy needs and air pollution at source. For example, each tonne of paper made from recycled waste paper instead of virgin wood saves over 50% of the energy needed to manufacture the paper and produces 75% less air pollution. See Chapter 6, "Garbage," and Chapter 11, "Garbage: Trim that Tonne," for more information on recycling.

- Transportation is a major source of nitrogen oxides emissions. Reduce your use of automobiles as much as possible; use public transit, bicycles or walk. Make sure that your car's pollution control equipment is working properly. See Chapter 15, "Transportation," for more suggestions.

- Acidic soil is more vulnerable to acid rain. Many chemical fertilizers increase the acidity of the soil. See Chapter 16, "Yard and Garden," for ways to avoid using chemicals on your garden.

- Awareness is the key to action. Stay informed about what the provincial and federal governments are doing about acid rain. Stay informed about the extent of the problem. Environment Canada monitors the pH of precipitation and will give you this information. (For Ontarians, the information is available every Saturday in the *Toronto Star*'s "Acid Rain Watch," included with the weather report.) Encourage your local paper to carry information on the acidity of rainfall in your area.

- Share information and encourage others to get involved. For example, if you have a cottage in an acid-sensitive area, you could contact your ministry of the environment for advice on monitoring the quality of your lake and getting other cottagers involved in fighting acid rain. Contact a local environment group or cottagers' association if you need more information.

- Write letters. Express your concern and your support for emission reductions to the provincial and federal governments; to major industrial sources (for example, Inco, Falconbridge, Ontario Hydro, Algoma Steel, Noranda, Hudson Bay Mining and Smelting); to the U.S. President and the U.S. Ambassador to Canada. (See source list for this chapter at the end of the book.)

- Give your financial support to environment groups fighting against acid rain. (See source list.)

The Greenhouse Effect: The Sky's the Limit

If the atmosphere was trying to get our attention, last summer [1988] was a public relations coup.
— MAX ALLEN, *IDEAS*, CBC RADIO

THE PROBLEM:

We are releasing heat-trapping gases into the atmosphere in sufficient concentrations to change the composition of the atmosphere. Moreover, we are cutting down the world's trees and not replanting. In both of these ways we are causing global warming, known as the greenhouse effect.

THE SOLUTION:

Reduce emissions of pollutants into the atmosphere, stop massive deforestation, and plant trees.

Since the Industrial Revolution, we have been using the atmosphere as a convenient dumping ground, spewing noxious and toxic wastes from smokestacks. Confident that the atmosphere can tolerate, dissipate or otherwise cope with the unwanted by-products of industry and fossil-fuel combustion, we continue to pump poisons into the air.

However, the hidden cost of our negligence is now coming to light. The greenhouse effect, and the resulting climate change, are rapidly being acknowledged as the most serious environmental threat to the global community.

DEFINITION

The warming of the earth's climate is an environmental catastrophe on a new scale, with the potential to violently disrupt virtually every natural ecosystem and many of the structures and institutions that humanity has grown to depend on.
— Lester R. Brown, et al., *State of the World 1989*

The greenhouse effect is caused by emissions of over 20 gases into the atmosphere. The major contributors are carbon dioxide (CO_2), ozone, methane, nitrous oxide and chlorofluorocarbons (CFCs). Although these gases are produced by many industrial processes, the major source is the burning of fossil fuels in boilers, furnaces and automobile engines. When released into the air in large quantities, these gases cause the earth's atmosphere to warm by trapping the sun's heat. Infrared radiation that would normally be reflected back into space hovers in the atmosphere, like a thick blanket over the earth.

The scientific explanation of this process is relatively straightforward. The sun's rays are able to travel through carbon dioxide (CO_2) and warm the earth's surface. The earth absorbs a certain amount of the sun's heat, but releases the excess in the form of infrared radiation. Because carbon dioxide absorbs infrared radiation, some of the excess heat is trapped in the atmosphere, rather than escaping into space. The amount of heat that stays near the earth's surface depends on the amount of CO_2 in the air: the greater the amount of CO_2, the greater the degree of heat that is trapped.

But carbon dioxide is only half the story. Other greenhouse gases, such as CFCs (found in air conditioners, refrigerators, some foams and aerosols, for example) may be less abundant than CO_2, but their power may be more destructive. Molecule for molecule, CFCs contribute 10,000 times more to the greenhouse effect than CO_2 because they are able to trap more of the heat radiated by the earth. Nitrous oxide (from vehicle exhaust, coal combustion and the use of fertilizers in agriculture) also contributes, as does methane (the primary component of natural gas, also produced by rotting garbage in landfill sites, by burning wood and vegetation and by bacteria in the guts of cattle). Methane traps 20 times more heat, molecule for molecule, than carbon dioxide.

Ozone, which in the upper atmosphere shields us from ultraviolet rays of the sun, at ground level is a greenhouse gas.

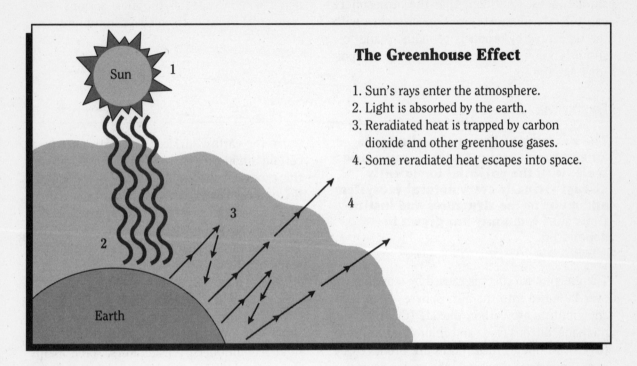

The Greenhouse Effect

1. Sun's rays enter the atmosphere.
2. Light is absorbed by the earth.
3. Reradiated heat is trapped by carbon dioxide and other greenhouse gases.
4. Some reradiated heat escapes into space.

CAUSES

The world's scientists are not united on the question of how much global warming has occurred, how long the climate change process will take, or what the exact results will be. Some say global warming has arrived; some say it never will be here; some have changed their minds from one argument to the other. However, everyone agrees that we are putting more and more carbon dioxide into the atmosphere. With our increased use of fossil fuels, the amount of CO_2 in the atmosphere is escalating at approximately 3 to 4% per decade.

In 1988, Canada contributed 116 million tonnes of carbon to the atmosphere from the combustion of fossil fuels, such as oil, gas and coal, to satisfy our energy demands. This figure

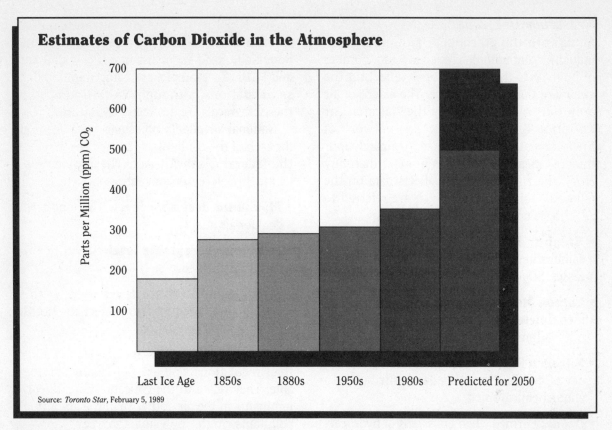

Estimates of Carbon Dioxide in the Atmosphere

Parts per Million (ppm) CO_2

700
600
500
400
300
200
100

Last Ice Age · 1850s · 1880s · 1950s · 1980s · Predicted for 2050

Source: *Toronto Star*, February 5, 1989

represents just 2% of the world's total emissions (from fossil fuel combustion) of over 5 billion tonnes (or 10,000 tonnes per minute of every day of the year). However, because Canada has just 0.5% of the world's population, our per capita output was more than 4 times higher than that of the average global citizen.

Emissions of greenhouse gases are accompanied by another major contributing factor: global deforestation. Plants absorb CO_2 from the atmosphere and store it as carbon in their tissues. When trees are cut down (as they are, worldwide, at an alarming rate — see the chapter on "Vanishing Forests"), not only are there fewer of them to absorb CO_2 from the atmosphere, but those that are felled release all the carbon they have absorbed while growing. In 1988, 0.4 billion to 2.5 billion tons of carbon were added to the atmosphere as a result of deforestation. Carbon dioxide is also released into the atmosphere when forests are cleared through burning.

Measuring Air Quality

Along with the greenhouse gases, Canadian industries and automobiles spew out a number of pollutants that are seriously affecting the quality of the air we breathe. The extent of air pollution is monitored by the National Air Pollution Surveillance (NAPS) network of Environment Canada. With approximately four hundred measuring stations in more than fifty cities, the NAPS network collects data on the following contaminants, which are referred to as "criteria pollutants":

- **Sulphur Dioxide (SO_2):** Formed by the combustion of fossil fuels and in smelting processes, SO_2 is a major contributor to acid rain.

- **Carbon Monoxide (CO):** This by-product of incomplete combustion comes most often from automobiles.

- **Nitrogen Dioxide (NO_2):** Primarily a product of combustion, this gas contributes to photochemical smog.

- **Ozone:** Formed when emissions of hydrocarbons and nitrogen oxides interact in the air, high levels of ozone pollution tend to occur on hot, bright, still days.

- **Total suspended particulates:** These are made up of a wide variety of particles, including lead, that remain suspended in the air.

The NAPS network is currently attempting to expand its measuring program to other potentially toxic air pollutants. Dioxins, furans and PCBs, for example, are being monitored at some stations, although NAPS findings on these chemicals are not regularly released.

National air quality objectives have been set for each of the contaminants listed above under the federal Clean Air Act. These objectives define three levels of concentration:

- **Maximum desirable level:** The long-term goal for air quality;

- **Maximum acceptable level:** Adequate protection against adverse effects;

- **Maximum tolerable level:** Beyond this level, action is required to protect the health of the general population.

The quality objectives are guidelines rather than regulations, and are not legally enforceable. They relate to the concentrations of contaminants in the air, rather than the amount of pollutants emitted by a single source.

The federal government sets the standards and each province has the choice of whether or not to adopt and enforce the limits.

Ozone: The Good and the Bad

The ozone layer filters out or reflects the sun's ultraviolet radiation, preventing most of these harmful rays from reaching the earth's surface. (See Chapter 3, "Losing the Ozone Layer," for information on how the protective ozone layer is being destroyed.)

Closer to the surface of the earth, however, increased concentration of ozone causes damage to vegetation and has been linked with human respiratory problems and lung ailments.

Peak levels of ozone pollution tend to occur on hot summer days, late in the afternoon when there is lots of traffic. The "maximum acceptable" level of ozone is 82 parts per billion (hourly average), but in 1988 this guideline was exceeded on 157 occasions in North York, Ontario, and 189 times in Windsor, Ontario, for example. The highest recorded reading of ozone in 1988 was 213 parts per billion in the Vancouver suburb of Port Coquitlam.

EFFECTS

Right now, air pollution is the only industrial commodity freely traded among all nations of the world.
— Eric Bailey in *Environment Views*, December, 1988

Climate change, like no other issue, calls the whole notion of human progress into question.
— Lester R. Brown, et al., *State of the World 1989*

The increase of atmospheric pollutants — especially CO_2 — in the atmosphere corresponds to an increase in the global average temperature. Over the past century there has been an observed increase of 0.5 to 0.7°C. In the 1890s, the global average temperature was 14.5°C; in the 1980s, the average is 15.2°C. The present global surface temperature is 0.4°C warmer than the mean values for the period of 1951-1980.

Although such statistics seem far removed from everyday experience, the sweltering heat in the summer of 1988 made the figures all too tangible. 1988 was the warmest year in recorded weather history. The next five warmest years have all occurred in the 1980s — 1987, 1983, 1981, 1980 and 1986.

Scientists predict that by 2050 average temperatures could be from 1.5 to 4.5°C higher than at present, or warmer than the earth has been in human history. (A change in global temperature of just 6°C separates ice ages from warmer periods.)

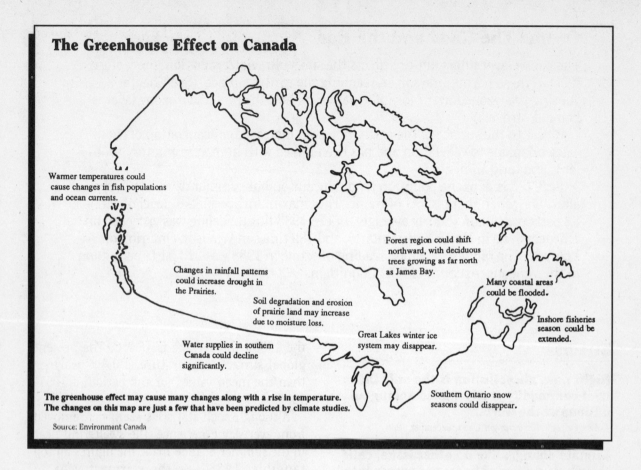

The Greenhouse Effect on Canada

Warmer temperatures could cause changes in fish populations and ocean currents.

Changes in rainfall patterns could increase drought in the Prairies.

Soil degradation and erosion of prairie land may increase due to moisture loss.

Water supplies in southern Canada could decline significantly.

Forest region could shift northward, with deciduous trees growing as far north as James Bay.

Many coastal areas could be flooded.

Inshore fisheries season could be extended.

Great Lakes winter ice system may disappear.

Southern Ontario snow seasons could disappear.

The greenhouse effect may cause many changes along with a rise in temperature. The changes on this map are just a few that have been predicted by climate studies.

Source: Environment Canada

The equatorial regions would see the least amount of temperature change, while countries in the northern hemisphere would have changes of approximately 3°C in the lower latitudes and up to 8°C in the higher latitudes. Although ecosystems adapt to gradual shifts in temperature, the predicted warming is 5 to 10 times faster than the temperature change of the past century.

Because Canada is a country of climatic extremes, it will be one of the areas most affected by global warming. As temperatures increase by just a few degrees, global wind and rainfall patterns will change, affecting Canada's agriculture and water resources. In southern Canadian agricultural areas, for example, severe droughts may be more frequent and fresh water supplies depleted. The rising sea level — the predicted result of the expansion of ocean water as it warms and the melting of glaciers in mountainous regions — could have a devastating effect on coastal lands and communities.

There are, in fact, scientific data suggesting that the global sea level is already rising. Two Canadian geophysicists from the University of Toronto reported in May 1989 that the global sea level is rising by between 2.0 mm and 2.4 mm a year.

Effects Predicted by the Worldwatch Institute

"A temperature increase of 1 degree Celsius per decade in mid- to upper latitudes translates into a shift in vegetation zones of 60–100 miles northward. Terrestrial ecosystems cannot migrate that fast. Vast numbers of trees are likely to die, and new trees adapted to warmer temperatures are unlikely to be able to replace them rapidly."

"Biological diversity, already being reduced by various human activities, may be one of the chief casualties of global warming. . . . Accelerated species extinction is an inevitable consequence of rapid warming."

"Sea level rise is another threat. . . . Studies conclude that a temperature rise of 3 degrees Celsius by 2050 would raise sea level by 50-100 centimeters. By the end of the next century, sea levels may be up by as much as two meters."

— Lester R. Brown, et al., *State of the World 1989*

Monitoring Change

Environment Canada has embarked on a number of studies to examine the impact that global warming will have on Canada. The results are published periodically in the *Climate Change Digest*.

The journal's mandate is clearly not to find solutions to the problem of global warming or to suggest policies to reduce emissions. Instead, with articles such as "Implications of Climate Change for Downhill Skiing in Quebec" and "Implications of Climate Change for Tourism and Recreation in Ontario," the journal looks at economic conditions and even economic "opportunities" that a warmer climate will bring to Canadians. Here is an example:

Climate change offers the potential for significant economic opportunity. For Canada, this is likely to include an extension of the growing season and year-round shipping on the Great Lakes. The key element in successfully adapting to these changes will be our ability to mitigate the negative effects and to take advantage of the benefits.

The same logic pervades many Environment Canada publications:

If we plan now for change, with effective responses and strategies, we can perhaps reduce the unfavourable effects and capitalize on the opportunities that a new climate will bring.

However, some might find it bizarre to contemplate how Canada's downhill skiing industry will be affected when the world as we know it will be changed irrevocably and nearly every living thing on earth affected.

Specific predictions of the effects that climate change will have on Canada include:

• Lower precipitation and higher temperatures may threaten the security of Canada's food supply;
• In Ontario, agricultural losses may be up to $100 million a year;
• In the Prairies, reduced wheat yields may result in losses of $160 million every year;
• In Atlantic Canada, several billion dollars could be lost because of sea level rise, which would threaten coastal communities.

SOLUTIONS

Climate change has so much momentum behind it now that it can only be slowed, not stopped.
— Lester R. Brown, et al., *State of the World 1989*

A major conference held in Toronto in June 1988 brought together scientists and policy-makers from forty-six countries to discuss a wide range of atmospheric problems such as acid rain, the greenhouse effect and depletion of the ozone layer. In its report, *The Changing*

Atmosphere, the conference issued a chilling and direct warning:

> Humanity is conducting an unintended, uncontrolled, globally pervasive experiment whose ultimate consequences could be second only to a global nuclear war. The Earth's atmosphere is being changed at an unprecedented rate by pollutants resulting from human activities, inefficient and wasteful fossil fuel use and the effects of rapid population growth in many regions. These changes represent a major threat to international security and are already having harmful consequences over many parts of the globe.

The result of the conference was a call for action, directed to all governments, international bodies, non-governmental organizations, industry, educational institutions and individuals. Specific goals are:

- To reduce global carbon dioxide emissions by 20% by the year 2005. (The conference statement acknowledges that a 50% cut will be needed just to stabilize atmospheric CO_2.)

- To increase funding for the development of renewable energy.
- To reduce deforestation and increase afforestation.
- To eliminate most uses of CFCs by the year 2000.
- To label products so that consumers can judge the extent of atmospheric contamination that arises from the manufacture and use of products.

The federal government responded to the conference's challenge by drafting plans to tighten car and truck emissions standards. The plans involve tougher limits on emissions of nitrogen oxides from gas or diesel engines. The limits, which include a 30% reduction of nitrogen oxides and a 20% curb on carbon dioxide emissions, go into effect on 1994 model cars.

However, the federal government has not adopted any specific strategy for reducing our carbon dioxide output by the 50% needed to stabilize CO_2.

What Can I Do?

- Greenhouse gases are accumulating in the atmosphere as a result of burning fossil fuels. Why do we burn such great quantities of fossil fuels? To meet our high energy demand. If we continue to consume energy at the present

rate, and if Canada's rate of growth continues in its present trend, our output of carbon dioxide by the year 2005 will be much greater than it was in 1985. For ways to reduce your energy use and to use energy more efficiently, see

Chapter 12, "Energy: Turning On Efficiency," Chapter 13, "Energy Conservation in the Home," and Chapter 15, "Transportation."

- Approximately 75% of ozone-forming pollutants come from automobile exhaust. Reduce your use of cars; use public transit, bicycle or walk instead. See Chapter 15, "Transportation," for more suggestions.

- Research into more environmentally benign sources of energy should be encouraged and supported by government and individuals. There are a number of non-profit groups in Canada promoting alternative energy and they are all in need of funding. (See source list for this chapter.)

- Write to the federal department of Energy, Mines and Resources and to your provincial Ministry of Energy to support research into and promotion of renewable energy sources that could end our dependence on fossil fuels. Alternative energy and energy conservation programs have been drastically cut in recent years, and it is only through the vocal support of Canadians for such programs that governments will take action.

- CFCs are not only contributing to the greenhouse effect, but they are also eating away the ozone layer. See Chapter 3, "Losing the Ozone Layer," for information on what you can do to stop the depletion of the ozone layer.

- Fight the massive global deforestation that is occurring. See Chapter 5, "Vanishing Forests," for ways that you can make a difference.

- Plant trees. This is just a stop-gap measure because trees release all of their stored carbon when they die. Nevertheless, every tonne of maple keeps approximately 2 tonnes of carbon dioxide out of the atmosphere, while the tree is alive. The United Nations Association in Canada (see source list) sponsors a tree-planting initiative in Africa. A donation ensures that trees will be planted in Ethiopia.

  In Ontario, the group Trees for Today and Tomorrow (see source list) has an "Adopt a Tree" program. Each donor receives a certificate for one free seedling from any White Rose Nursery. The trees are planted on highly eroded riverbanks, in an attempt to stabilize the soil.

  Phone your city's Public Works Department; some cities will plant tree seedlings on your property at no cost.

Losing the Ozone Layer: What You Can't See Can Hurt You

We began to notice a bite out of the ozone profile just as though Mr. Pac-Man had been at work.
— Dr. Wayne Evans, *Globe and Mail*, February 1989

The Problem:

Synthetic chemicals are destroying the ozone layer, which protects the earth from the sun's ultraviolet rays.

The Solution:

Stop producing and releasing ozone-depleting chemicals. The need for action is urgent: even if all of these chemicals were banned today, thinning of the ozone layer would continue for close to 100 years.

When chlorofluorocarbons (CFCs) were invented in 1928, they were touted as the "perfect" industrial chemicals: they are long-lasting (with a life span of 100 years or more), they are non-toxic and don't accumulate at ground level, and they are excellent heat absorbers for refrigeration.

It was not until the 1970s that scientists discovered another characteristic of CFCs: they destroy the ozone layer, the thin shield that protects the earth from the sun's ultraviolet (UV-B) rays. And it was not until the 1980s that scientists made another surprising discovery: there was a "hole" as high as Mount Everest and the size of the United States in the ozone layer over Antarctica.

DEFINITION

The ozone layer is in the stratosphere, between 15 and 35 km above the earth's surface. Although it is approximately 20 km thick, the ozone layer is not densely concentrated: if the entire layer were compressed to ground-level pressure, it would form a band only 3 mm thick. It is this relatively thin band that shields the earth and absorbs ultraviolet light as the sun's rays enter the upper atmosphere.

But the ozone layer is being destroyed by a group of chemicals that do not exist naturally. Ozone-destroying chemicals include halons (used in fire extinguishers), and the industrial chemicals methyl chloroform and carbon tetrachloride. However, the major culprits are chlorofluorocarbons.

When CFCs were developed in the 1930s, they were considered to be safe and efficient refrigerants. In the 1950s, they were incorporated as blowing agents in the production of plastic foam. And in the 1970s, thousands of tonnes of CFCs were released directly into the lower atmosphere when they were used as propellants in aerosol spray cans.

After being released, CFCs take from 10 to 100 years to reach the upper atmosphere, where the chemicals are broken apart by the ultraviolet light of the sun. As the chemicals break down, chlorine is released from CFC molecules. Similarly, bromine is released from halons. Chlorine and bromine are the chemicals that eat away the ozone layer. A single atom of chlorine is capable of destroying from 10,000 to 100,000 molecules of ozone; bromine is up to 10 times more destructive to ozone than is chlorine.

F. Sherwood Rowland, a University of California scientist, first asked the seemingly benign question: What happens to CFCs when they reach the upper atmosphere? Reflecting upon his discovery that these chemicals destroy the ozone layer, Rowland reports that "There was no moment when I yelled 'Eureka.' I just came home one night and told my wife, 'The work is going very well, but it looks like the end of the world.'"

Source: Lydia Dotto and Harold Schiff, *The Ozone War*

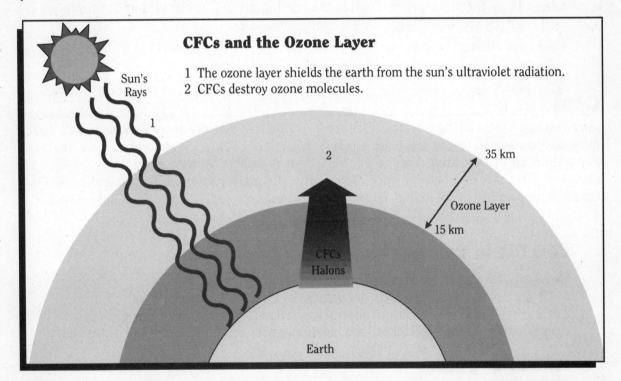

CFCs and the Ozone Layer

1 The ozone layer shields the earth from the sun's ultraviolet radiation.
2 CFCs destroy ozone molecules.

Sun's Rays

35 km
Ozone Layer
15 km

CFCs Halons

Earth

CFCs also contribute to global climate change, and are known as "greenhouse" gases. (See the previous chapter, "The Greenhouse Effect.") Although CFCs are less abundant in the atmosphere than carbon dioxide, their effect on global warming is 10,000 times more powerful, molecule for molecule, because CFCs trap more heat in the atmosphere. CFCs contribute approximately 25% of the current greenhouse effect.

Convenience Costs

In Canada, foam food packages (including disposable cups) are no longer made with CFCs. The chemical HCFC-22, which has one-twentieth of the ozone depletion potential of CFCs, is used by most manufacturers instead.

However, when CFCs were used extensively, one billion chlorofluorocarbon molecules were trapped in the foam of one take-out cup made with CFCs. When the disposable cup was thrown away and either burned or crushed, the CFCs were released into the atmosphere. Each of the one billion CFC molecules in the cup could destroy approximately 100,000 ozone molecules.

Source: Curtis A. Moore in *International Wildlife*, March/April, 1989

CAUSES

Approximately 80% of the world's CFCs are made and consumed in the developed world. More than 16 billion kilograms of ozone-depleting chemicals have been produced since the 1930s. Approximately 1.1 million tonnes are produced globally every year, and since 1978, levels of CFCs in the atmosphere have increased at a rate of 5 to 6% every year.

Canada is responsible for just under 3% of the world's chlorofluorocarbon use and emissions.

CFC Use in Canada

Refrigerators and Air Conditioners
CFCs are used as heat absorbers or coolants in refrigerators and air conditioners. CFCs are released into the air in several ways: during the manufacturing process, through leaks in the appliances, or when appliances are thrown out and destroyed.

Foam Blowing Agents
CFCs are used to expand some liquid plastics into hard and soft foams for products such as packaging, cushions and insulation. (Not all foams are produced using CFCs.) In the production of flexible foam, CFCs are released directly into the atmosphere; in the production of rigid foam, most of the CFCs are trapped in the foam cells. When the foam is thrown out and crushed, CFCs are released.

Solvents

CFCs are used for cleaning some computer microchips and circuit boards. Most of the CFCs evaporate into the atmosphere during the cleaning process. CFCs are also used in some dry-cleaning fluids.

Aerosols

CFCs are used as the propellant in some aerosol sprays. Ozone-destroying chemicals are released into the atmosphere each time the spray is used. In March 1980, the use of CFCs in hair sprays, antiperspirants and deodorants was banned in Canada. Although the ban accounted for a temporary national reduction of CFCs by 45%, this decrease was quickly eroded by increases in industrial uses. However, the aerosol industry continued to switch to other propellants and by 1989, only 1 to 2% of all aerosols produced in Canada contained CFCs.

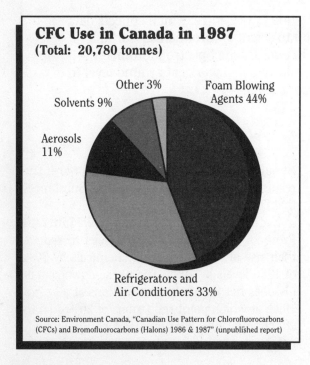

CFC Use in Canada in 1987
(Total: 20,780 tonnes)

Other 3%

Solvents 9%

Foam Blowing Agents 44%

Aerosols 11%

Refrigerators and Air Conditioners 33%

Source: Environment Canada, "Canadian Use Pattern for Chlorofluorocarbons (CFCs) and Bromofluorocarbons (Halons) 1986 & 1987" (unpublished report)

EFFECTS

When British scientists reported in 1985 that a hole in the ozone layer over Antarctica had been occurring each spring since 1979, the news came as a complete surprise.
— Lester R. Brown, et al., *State of the World 1989*

A dramatic thinning occurs every year in the ozone layer over the Arctic and Antarctic. The thinning recurs at fluctuating levels during the polar spring. The "hole" lasts for approximately two months and then fills in.

In Antarctica scientists have measured ozone depletion of 30 to 50% during the worst of the thinning process, and in some places the ozone layer has temporarily disappeared altogether. In October 1987 the ozone layer over Antarctica was depleted by 95%. A smaller hole has been discovered in the Arctic.

Between 1979 and 1986 the average global ozone levels dropped by 5%.

What does this mean in terms of human health? For every 1% drop in ozone, levels of non-melanoma skin cancer are projected to rise by approximately 4 to 6%. As more ultraviolet radiation reaches the earth, the incidence of eye cataracts is also expected to rise. There is evidence that increases in ultraviolet radiation suppress the human immune system, leading to greater susceptibility to disease.

Crops are also adversely affected by increased levels of ultraviolet radiation. Particularly at risk are the world's major food crops: wheat, rice, corn and soya beans. Growth of phytoplankton — microscopic ocean organisms that are an essential link in the food chain — is reduced by higher levels of ultraviolet radiation.

Brewer Ozone Spectrophotometer

Environment Canada operates the World Ozone Data Centre, which collects data on the ozone layer and provides information to scientists around the world. It relies on a recent Canadian invention, the Brewer Ozone Spectrophotometer — the world's most accurate ozone-measuring device, that works at ground level to measure the height and thickness of the ozone layer.

SOLUTIONS

International boundaries are irrelevant in the stratosphere: each country's production and use of ozone-depleting chemicals contribute to the destruction of the ozone layer. In recognition of the global nature of the problem, the United Nations Environment Programme convened an international meeting of scientists and policymakers in Montreal in September 1987. The goal was to produce the first international treaty to protect the atmosphere; the result was the Montreal Protocol on Substances that Deplete the Ozone Layer.

Nations that have signed the Montreal Protocol, including Canada, agreed to reduce their use of ozone-depleting chemicals by 50% of 1986 levels by 1999. The phase-down schedule does not require any reductions at all until 1993, at which point reductions of 20% go into effect. By 1999, participating countries will reduce their use of CFCs by 50%. Third World nations have a different reduction schedule under the Montreal Protocol, allowing them higher levels of consumption of ozone-depleting chemicals.

Written into the agreement is a provision to strengthen the protocol if scientific evidence shows that more controls are needed. In fact, the agreement was based on an estimated 1.5% drop in Arctic ozone, which has since been proven to be too low. Ozone reductions of 2.5 to 6.5% have been measured in northernmost areas. Countries participating in the Montreal Protocol will meet in 1990 to consider revisions to the agreement.

"On October 17-18, 1988, during the science meeting in The Hague, we heard a consensus scientific viewpoint that said that even if all nations of the world complied with the control measures currently set out in the Montreal Protocol, the Antarctic hole would remain forever. They went on to say that the hole will not disappear until we reduce current emission levels by greater than 85%...close to a complete phase-out of currently regulated substances."

— G. Victor Buxton, Environment Canada, November 30, 1988

"In the end, it may be safer and cheaper, if inconvenient, to cope with ozone depletion by wearing wide-brimmed hats, sunglasses and sunscreen."

— Philip Elmer-Dewitt in *TIME*, January 2, 1989

Different levels of government and various sectors of industry are responding to the dire warnings of scientists. Although Environment Canada has stated that "an immediate ban on the production and use of all CFCs and halons... would have unacceptably high social costs," the federal government has called for an 85% elimination of ozone-depleting chemicals by 1999, with the remaining 15% to be phased out as safe alternatives become available. However, environment groups such as Friends of the Earth are calling for a complete phase-out by 1995, and for other ozone-depleting chemicals, such as methyl chloroform, to be added to the Montreal Protocol.

At a provincial level, a number of governments are considering legislation to protect the ozone layer. Ontario industries produce over half of the ozone-depleting chemicals in Canada, but there are plans to place a ban on most uses by 1991. Until alternatives are found in the refrigeration industry, legislation will require that manufacturers collect and recycle the CFCs that are trapped in appliances.

In an unprecedented display of thinking globally and acting locally, the City of Toronto has banned within the city's boundaries the manufacture of CFC-based products unless no alternatives exist.

Industries are now attempting to get a jump on legislation and to respond to mounting consumer pressure. Provigo, the supermarket chain based in Quebec, was the first major food retailer to ban CFC-based packaging from store shelves. Lily Cups, which produces one-quarter of Canada's foam cups, took just four weeks to eliminate CFCs from its manufacturing process. Dow Chemical, the manufacturer of STYROFOAM, phased out the use of CFCs in 1989.

Fast food chains such as McDonald's, Kentucky Fried Chicken and Burger King have switched from CFC packaging.

Unfortunately, some of the alternatives to CFCs may have serious drawbacks. Known as "soft" CFCs, the alternative chemicals are members of the same chemical family as chlorofluorocarbons. Although some (hydrofluorocarbons or HFCs, now being developed) may not deplete the ozone layer at all, and some (hydrochlorofluorocarbons or HCFCs) may deplete it far less than CFCs, there are other concerns. In particular, the "soft" CFCs may contribute to global warming, especially since their use will now increase. Groups such as Friends of the Earth do not view "soft" CFCs as a solution. They recommend that industries and governments focus research and development efforts on completely non-CFC alternatives.

"No one argued more passionately and more persuasively for the benefits of the fluorocarbon spray can than Robert Abplanalp, its inventor and manufacturer, and the person who stood to lose most by its demise. Although environmentalists claimed that the fluorocarbons emitted during spraying could result in a rash of skin cancers by destroying the atmosphere's ozone layer, Abplanalp for years was able to refute the findings of some of the world's most eminent scientists. Finally, the weight of scientific evidence became so overwhelming the U.S. Food and Drug Administration could dawdle no longer: it announced that the fluorocarbon spray can would be banned. The very next day, Robert Abplanalp was pleased to announce the introduction of a new spray can which not only did away with the feared fluorocarbons but also outperformed the old spray can."

— Lawrence Solomon, *The Conserver Solution*

What Can I Do?

• The power of the consumer has been clearly demonstrated on the front lines of the "ozone war." Public opinion and concerns *can* direct company policy: many manufacturers have responded to the pressures and challenges that they have been receiving from their customers. Cascade Dominion, for example, a large manufacturer of egg cartons, decided to switch from polystyrene foam to paper cartons at its Ontario plant because of consumer complaints.

Voice your concerns about depletion of the ozone layer at the supermarket. Ask the manager if a product's foam packaging has been produced using CFCs. The manager might not know the answer, but you are helping to raise awareness about the issue. Better yet, write to the company that manufactures that product. If you can't be sure that the foam was made without CFCs, avoid buying the product. Ask the store manager to sell eggs in paper cartons. Buy fruit and vegetables in bulk rather than in foam trays.

• According to the Canadian Aerosol Information Bureau, less than 1% of all aerosol products in Canada contain CFCs. Contact the bureau to find out which products contain CFCs. Avoid buying these products and ask your store manager to stop stocking them.

• Until refrigerators and air conditioners that don't use ozone-depleting chemicals are on the market, there are a few steps you can take. The most important is to ensure that your appliances don't leak, are serviced properly and disposed of safely. Freon in refrigerator coils will escape into the atmosphere if the walls of the freezer are punctured (a good reason *not* to use a knife to dislodge ice when defrosting). If a new compressor is being installed or freon replaced in your appliance, make sure that the old material is returned to the manufacturer for recycling or safe disposal. It should not be simply vented into the air. If you are throwing out an old fridge, call the manufacturer and ask to have the CFCs drained and recycled. If the manufacturer won't take the fridge, call a few second-hand stores. Even if you're not successful, you will help get the message across to manufacturers.

• Consider installing a ceiling fan instead of an air conditioner.

• Car and truck air conditioners use the worst, most destructive CFC available — CFC-12. Is the convenience worth it? If you have an air conditioner in your car and it needs servicing, make your concerns about the ozone layer known to the mechanic. Phone around and you may find a repair centre that will recycle the coolant instead of letting the chemicals escape. General Motors, for example, has installed recycling machines at most of its large dealerships. (It's interesting to note that the state of Vermont has banned the sale and registration of all automobiles with CFC-containing air conditioners, starting with 1993 models.) See Chapter 15, "Transportation," for ways to keep your car cool without buying an air conditioner.

- Most disposable foam cups are manufactured without CFCs, but they are still disposable and therefore should be avoided. (See Chapter 11, "Garbage.")

- When buying furniture, avoid cushions, mattresses and moulded frames made with foam, unless you're sure that the manufacturer does not use CFCs. Spring mattresses, feather pillows, and wooden furniture frames are just three examples of alternatives.

- Insulate with cellulose or fibreglass rather than rigid foam, or make sure that the rigid-foam manufacturer does not use CFCs.

- When buying a hand-held fire extinguisher, shop around for one that does not contain ozone-damaging halons.

- Join the Friends of the Earth's Ozone Protection Campaign. The organization has produced an Ozone Protection Kit, with background information and suggestions for action. Display your "I'm an Ozone Protector" decal where it will be noticed. Friends of the Earth also sells a T-shirt that declares "Protect the Ozone."

- Send for a copy of the booklet, *Protecting the Ozone Layer: What You Can Do*, published by the Environmental Defense Fund in the United States. The booklet lists products, actions and alternatives. (See source list for this chapter for address.)

- Send for a copy of the Worldwatch Institute's comprehensive overview of the science and politics of the ozone depletion issue, *Protecting Life on Earth: Steps to Save the Ozone Layer* by Cynthia Pollock Shea, Worldwatch Paper 87. Friends of the Earth is the official distributor in Canada. (See source list.)

- Write to the federal Minister of the Environment in support of an immediate 85% cut in CFC production in Canada and a complete elimination by 1995. (This is the level of reduction that is necessary, although the Montreal Protocol calls for only a 50% cut by 1999.) Urge that Canada take a vocal stance in strengthening the Montreal Protocol.

- Write to your provincial environment ministry and find out what regulations are in place in your province to protect the ozone layer. Urge the provincial government to institute mandatory recycling of CFCs in appliances and automobiles. For information about legislation, you can also contact Friends of the Earth.

- Let other people know about your concerns. Friends of the Earth has produced a slide show, *Ozone Alert*, that they will lend to educators. The United Church of Canada has made a video version of *Ozone Alert*, which is available at church outlets across the country. For more information contact The United Church of Canada, 85 St. Clair Avenue East, Toronto, Ontario M4T 1M8; (416) 925-5931.

Water: Swimmable, Drinkable, Fishable?

When I first became involved in the Niagara River issue ten years ago, I thought it would simply be a matter of identifying the problem and then convincing governments and industry to sit down and work out the most expeditious solution. How naive I was! The problems have long since been identified, and the solutions have long since been available, but the pollution goes on and the degradation of our precious fresh-water resource continues unabated.

— MARGHERITA HOWE, OPERATION CLEAN (NIAGARA), *PROBE POST*, WINTER 1989

THE PROBLEM:

We are treating all water resources — oceans, lakes, rivers, groundwater — as if they are never-ending sources of clean water that can withstand any amount of contamination.

THE SOLUTION:

Stop releasing pollutants into waterways, into the air (they may eventually settle in water) or into the ground (they may make their way into streams and lakes, or filter down into the groundwater). Recognize that fresh water is a valuable resource not to be wasted.

Without water, no living thing can survive. Three hundred and twenty-six million cubic miles of water cover the earth, but only 3% of the available supply is fresh rather than salt water. Canada has one-fifth of the world's supply of fresh water, most of it contained in the Great Lakes.

Water is a universal solvent: it absorbs and carries away with it something of everything it touches. It is precisely this quality that has loaded oceans, lakes, rivers, streams and groundwater with the contaminants we dump into the environment.

Freshwater and Land by Province and Territory

	Land (km²)	Freshwater (km²)
Northwest Territories	3,293,020	133,300
Yukon Territory	478,970	4,480
British Columbia	929,730	18,070
Alberta	644,390	16,800
Saskatchewan	570,700	81,630
Manitoba	548,360	101,590
Ontario	891,190	177,390
Quebec	1,356,790	183,890
New Brunswick	72,090	1,350
Nova Scotia	52,840	2,650
Prince Edward Island	5,660	—
Newfoundland and Labrador	371,690	34,030
Total	9,215,430	755,180

Source: Energy, Mines and Resources Canada

Canadian Water Facts

- Approximately 7.6% of Canada is covered by fresh water, enough to flood the entire country to a depth of more than 2 m.
- Approximately 30% of Canada's fresh water is in the Yukon and Northwest Territories.
- Two-thirds of Canada's river-flow is northward; 80% of the population lives in the southern part of the country, within 20 km of the U.S. border.
- Canada has over 200,000 km of coastline.

- All of Great Britain would fit into the Great Lakes.
- Every day, the average Canadian uses 260 litres of water for domestic purposes, and another 6,400 litres indirectly for agriculture, industry and mining.
- Over a lifetime, an average Canadian uses approximately 7 million litres of water, nearly half of which is used for flushing toilets.

DEFINITION

Pollutants enter waterways either directly or indirectly: directly when dumped into a body of water, or indirectly through runoff from fields, slow seepage from aging waste sites, or the settling of airborne chemicals, for example. The pollution may be deliberate, as is the case in much of the documented ocean dumping, or it may be accidental — when there is an oil spill, for example.

In the 1960s and 1970s, the problem of water pollution made headlines when Lake Erie was pronounced "dead." Excessive nutrients, especially phosphates in detergents, were causing algae blooms that depleted the oxygen in the water.

Although the source of the pollution was identified and the amount of phosphates limited, another "invisible" problem was threatening water supplies. The extent of this problem is just now being recognized. Many toxic chemicals that enter waterways bind themselves to sediment particles. They then remain on the bottom of a lake or river until the sediment is disturbed. When stirred up through dredging, for example, the toxins are re-sus-pended in the water, where they may be absorbed by fish and plants or make their way into drinking water supplies. Not only is this problem much more difficult to identify, analyze and attribute to one source; it is also almost impossible to rectify.

CAUSES

Sewage
In 1984 only 2,164 of Canada's 3,250 communities had sewers. Of these 2,164, only 1,442 had some kind of sewage treatment facilities. In terms of population, only 57% of Canadians are served by wastewater treatment plants; another 28% are served by sewage collection, which is then sent untreated into rivers, lakes and oceans.

The Halifax area, for example, dumps almost 182 million litres of untreated domestic sewage and industrial waste into the Halifax Harbour *every day*. Victoria, British Columbia, dumps over 60 million litres a day into the Strait of Juan de Fuca. Quebec City dumps 51 tonnes of suspended solids and 500 million litres of untreated water a day into the St. Lawrence

River (the same river from which three million people get their drinking water).

To compound the problem, even when sewage is treated, the "purification" process removes only the solids, allowing for the decomposition of ordinary organic wastes and the killing of bacteria. Sewage treatment is designed for household wastes rather than industrial discharges; toxic contaminants, such as heavy metals, solvents, pesticides and industrial chemicals, are not removed during the process.

In Ontario alone, an estimated 12,000 industries discharge chemical wastes into municipal sewer systems. This, ironically, makes treated sewage one of the biggest sources of toxic contamination in the Great Lakes. In Nova Scotia almost a quarter of the hazardous waste generated in Halifax and Dartmouth in 1986 was put into the sewer system. In Manitoba, approximately 10,000 tonnes of hazardous wastes were dumped into the sewer system in 1985. According to Environment Quebec, industries in the province produce more than 350,000 tonnes of toxic waste every year, and approximately one-third of this chemical waste is dumped into the St. Lawrence River.

The by-product of the sewage treatment process — sludge (treated sewage solids) — is also a problem. Full of toxic contaminants, half a million tonnes of sewage sludge produced annually in Canada is either sent to landfill sites (where it may leach into the groundwater), burned (releasing dioxins into the air) or spread, as fertilizer, on agricultural land (where it may contaminate crops).

Excerpts from the Ecology Action Centre's History of the Halifax Harbour

1749 — Sir Edmund Cornwallis founded Halifax, emptied his chamberpot into the harbour.

1800-1900 — Over 50 combined (storm and raw) sewers built to flush directly into the harbour.

1970 — Halifax's *MacLaren Report* recommends filling in Purcell's Cove to build a primary treatment plant.

March 1989 — Municipalities agree to form Harbour Cleanup Corporation (a Crown corporation).

April 1989 — Bedford Institute of Oceanography releases the first of its harbour studies showing significant historical heavy metal pollution lying in sediment on the floor of the harbour inside McNabs Island.

May 1989 — A Halifax MLA flushes his toilet in Leiblen Park; 19.5 hours later the contents spill into the harbour. The Halifax MLA's contribution is added to that of 260,000 people living and working in the Halifax-Dartmouth metropolitan region, and to the 44 million gallons of wastewater generated by them every day.

Source: Ecology Action Centre, *Waste Facts: Save the Harbour, Save the Basin*

Airborne Contaminants

Chemicals in the air may eventually settle in waterways. The presence of the pesticide toxaphene in Lake Superior is an example of long-range, airborne contamination. Toxaphene was used to control pests in cotton crops in the American South. Although it has been restricted in Canada since 1971, this chemical is a pollutant in Lake Superior.

EFFECTS

The Great Lakes

More than 40 million people live near the Great Lakes and more than half derive their drinking water from the lakes — water that carries away waste from 20% of American industrial activity and 50% of Canadian industrial activity.

Approximately 1,000 industrial and commercial chemicals are present in the Great Lakes

Tonnes of Some Airborne Pollutants Entering the Great Lakes (1986)

	Superior	Michigan	Huron	Erie	Ontario
PCBs	9.8	6.9	7.2	3.1	2.3
DDT	0.58	0.40	0.43	0.19	0.14
Dieldrin	0.54	0.38	0.55	0.17	0.13
PAHs	163	114	118	51	38
Lead	1,230	1,730	596	754	379
Copper	821	575	298	151	95
Cadmium	82	58	60	75	28

Source: Pollution Probe, *The Great Lakes Primer*

Striking evidence of our failure to control the pollutants entering Canada's waterways is provided by two facts:

• The Great Lakes are now a *source* of pollution: toxins evaporate from the surfaces of the lakes and enter the atmosphere.

• The Beluga whales in the St. Lawrence River are so full of toxic contaminants that their bodies are treated as hazardous waste.

ecosystem. Of these chemicals, 400 are known to be toxic; at least 300 have been found in the bodies of Great Lakes fish.

According to the Environment Canada report *Toxic Chemicals in the Great Lakes Ecosystem*, the Lake Ontario-St. Lawrence River basin contains the highest rates of cancer in Canada, and within the area, cancer peaks are associated with toxic hotspots (areas with high levels of toxins). A joint report by the U.S. National Research Council and the Royal Society of Canada con-cluded that living in the Great Lakes basin exposes a person to "substantially higher levels of environmental contaminants" than those that occur in any other place on the continent.

Studies of this sort do not prove any direct connection between toxins and health because there are too many variables and many other possible sources of contamination. However, the association of toxic chemicals and increased incidence of cancer is clearly of concern, even if it is impossible to define scientifically the exact degree of risk.

Toxins: From Water to the Food Chain

"Once the chemicals enter the lake, they settle into the sediment and contaminate the bottom life. Aquatic plants, insects and other small organisms absorb the poisons. A single fish may consume hundreds of contaminated insects. The toxic chemicals in each insect are stored in the fish's body. A larger fish may eat dozens of these chemical-laden fish and absorb the poison from each into its own tissues. Herring gulls, feeding on the larger fish, may build up even higher levels of toxins. At each step in this food chain, the toxic chemicals are passed along and concentrated at increasingly dangerous levels. Chemicals, such as PCBs, have been found in the eggs of herring gulls in concentrations of over 100,000 times the level that is in the lake water."

— Environment Canada, *Toxic Chemicals* (Great Lakes Information Sheet)

Groundwater

You can drill a well in most parts of southern Canada and strike water of the highest quality within 20 metres of the surface.... However, all is not well in the underground world that yields water of such quality....

— Conservation Council of New Brunswick, *The Groundwater Pollution Primer*

Underlying most of the ground in Canada are aquifers, or underground "veins," that yield water to wells. Rainfall filters through the earth, making its way to the aquifer, where groundwater slowly moves (sometimes just a few centimetres a year) towards lakes and rivers.

According to the Science Council of Canada report *Water 2020*, "as many as a million

Reliance on Groundwater in Canada

Figures indicate the numbers of people and percentage of population using groundwater in each province or territory.

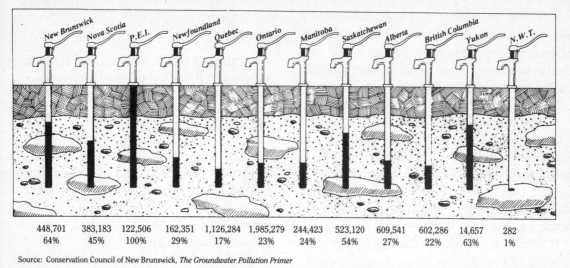

New Brunswick	Nova Scotia	P.E.I.	Newfoundland	Quebec	Ontario	Manitoba	Saskatchewan	Alberta	British Columbia	Yukon	N.W.T.
448,701	383,183	122,506	162,351	1,126,284	1,985,279	244,423	523,120	609,541	602,286	14,657	282
64%	45%	100%	29%	17%	23%	24%	54%	27%	22%	63%	1%

Source: Conservation Council of New Brunswick, *The Groundwater Pollution Primer*

Canadians may already be risking their health by drinking contaminated groundwater." Just as rainwater seeps into the ground, so do chemicals and contaminants from a variety of sources: agricultural fertilizers, pesticides and herbicides; chemicals in waste disposal sites; leaking underground storage tanks, such as those found at gas stations; leaking septic systems; road salts; and acid rain, for example.

Once groundwater is contaminated, there is no way to clean it up and, depending on the chemical, the groundwater may remain contaminated for generations. From the few studies that have been done, it is impossible to estimate the extent of groundwater contamination in Canada. However, those same few studies have yielded disturbing results.

In the Maritimes extensive groundwater testing has been done for the potato insecticide aldicarb. Of 197 wells tested in Prince Edward Island, 43 contained aldicarb; in New Brunswick, 9 out of 52 wells sampled contained the insecticide. In Ontario, 30 wells were tested for the herbicide atrazine, and 11 wells showed contamination. In British Columbia, 9 out of 21 wells tested contained the soil fumigant D-D. When one considers the extent of chemical applications to agricultural crops (80,000 tonnes of chemical fertilizers are spread in the Maritimes alone every year), it is not surprising that some of the chemicals seep into the groundwater.

Added to chemicals that are intentionally applied are those that are spilt accidentally. Leaking underground storage tanks are of particular concern. In fact, Environment Canada publishes a newsletter devoted to this topic — *LUST* or *Leaking Underground Storage Tanks*.

Gas stations usually store fuel in underground storage tanks that were installed in the 1950s and 60s. Most of the tanks were made from unprotected steel, which is now beginning to rust through. Environment Canada estimates that between 5 and 10% of all tanks — perhaps as many as 20,000 — are leaking.

It takes just one litre of gasoline to contaminate up to one million litres of groundwater. Over 1,000 wells in the Maritimes have been contaminated by leaking tanks since 1979, rendering the water unfit for human consumption. Add to this the hundreds of thousands of outdoor home heating-oil tanks, which may be leaking or may be improperly filled, causing spills.

Add also the hundreds of thousands of dumps and landfill sites that were used before proper controls were installed to protect the groundwater from contaminant leaching. And the abandoned coal-tar storage sites. And the millions of tonnes of salt that are dumped onto Canadian roads every winter. And the chemicals that seep down from cultivated fields. They all add up to a massive problem that is just now beginning to be monitored. According to the Science Council

of Canada, "The full extent of groundwater contamination in Canada is unknown and predictions of future contamination have not been made at either a provincial or national level."

Oceans

Dumping at sea is permitted only in cases where the disposal of wastes meets... regulatory requirements and no other environmentally preferable and practical alternative is available.
— Environment Canada, *Keeping the Ocean Clean*

Ocean dumping is regulated by Environment Canada through a system of permits and inspections. In 1986 a total of 168 permits were issued and used: they included 127 permits for dumping dredged material, 23 for dumping vessels, 1 for fire arms and prohibited weapons, 1 for construction rubble, and 1 for small quantities of radioactive material (for experimental purposes). 28% of the 1986–87 dumping operations were inspected.

Although industrial dumping is regulated, a much larger problem exists in the accidental or illegal dumping of materials at sea. According to a recent Greenpeace study, accidents involving nuclear-powered ships and submarines or aircraft carrying nuclear weapons have deposited 48 nuclear weapons and seven nuclear reactors on the bottom of the oceans. (There are approximately 550 nuclear reactors and 16,000 nuclear weapons aboard the ships and submarines of the U.S., Soviet, British, French and Chinese navies, according to Greenpeace.)

Plastic debris and litter are also serious problems in the marine environment. Balloons released for celebrations often end up in the ocean, where fish and mammals may eat them and choke to death. Buoys, beer cans and plastic packaging wash ashore on the coasts regularly.

SOLUTIONS

The annual expenditure of $20 billion necessary to provide all people on Earth with safe drinking water and adequate sewage treatment by 1990 represents about 4 per cent of annual global military expenditure.
— Science Council of Canada, *Water 2020*

Canadian water is at once the world's best bargain and the worst delusion, for we pay dearly in the long run for such short sightedness.... In no part of Canada is fresh water so plentiful that it can continue to be over-used and abused in the way it has been in recent decades. We must start viewing it as a scarce commodity that has real value. And we should begin managing it accordingly.
— Tom McMillan, former Environment Minister of Canada in *Environment Update*

Canadian water prices are lower than those in most developed countries. The price of water in Canada — 33 cents per cubic metre — is artificially low (compared with $4 in parts of the United States and $7 in Japan). Perhaps as a result of the low cost and perceived abundance, our per capita water consumption is the second highest in the world. Only U.S. consumption is higher. However, fresh water is an increasingly threatened resource: our consumption patterns will have to change, pricing policies will have to be adjusted to reflect the true cost of clean water, and our polluting habits will have to stop.

The responsibility for cleaning up the oceans, lakes, rivers and streams falls on many different levels of government. Instead of forming a concerted effort, the involvement of different levels seems to muddy the issue. In the Great Lakes area, for example, the jurisdictions involved in decision-making and problem-solving include two national governments (the United States and Canada), eight states, two provinces, three tribal councils, and many municipalities, each with sub-agencies responsible in some way for water quality.

Although there are a number of official agreements between the different parties (for example, the Great Lakes Water Quality Agreement between the U.S. and Canada, an agreement created by the International Joint Commission, which has representatives from both countries), there are no legal mechanisms to enforce the intentions of the agreements.

On the other hand, those intentions are spelled out explicitly. According to the 1909 Boundary Waters Treaty between the United States and Canada (which is still in effect today), "boundary waters and water flowing across the boundary shall not be polluted on either side to the injury of health or property on the other side." The 1978 Great Lakes Water Quality Agreement between the two countries calls for zero discharge of toxic substances in toxic amounts into the ecosystem.

What action is being taken to meet these agreements? The International Joint Commission and the Water Quality Board have established 42 "Areas of Concern" on the Great Lakes, 17 of which are in Canada. These areas are designated for investigation and clean-up, and the federal, provincial and native governments (11 of the 17 Areas of Concern are near or adjacent to reserves) are drawing up Remedial Action Plans that identify specific measures needed to control pollution and remove existing contamination. Once the Remedial Action Plans are completed in 1990, the real action of cleaning up will finally begin. As well, in October 1989 the federal government announced a 5-year, $125 million program for cleaning up the Great Lakes.

The Ontario government has also initiated the MISA (Municipal/Industrial Strategy for Abatement) program to reduce water pollution from industrial and municipal dischargers. This is the first time in the province that toxic pollution will be reduced at source, and the goal of the program is the virtual elimination of persistent toxic contaminants from all discharges into Ontario waterways. However, the limits are based on the "best available pollution control technology which is economically achievable"; in other words, pollution is defined by the economic bottom line.

The Government of Quebec and the federal government have entered into a joint agreement to clean up the St. Lawrence River, which provides drinking water for just under half of the population of Quebec. At a cost of over $110 million over 5 years, the action plan aims to identify industrial polluters and to negotiate a clean-up agreement with each, based on the "polluter pays principle."

Drinking Water

I don't use the word *safe*; I prefer to say the water is acceptable.
— Kate Davies, Toronto Department of Public Health, in *Toronto Star*

The federal and provincial governments in Canada have never set enforceable water quality standards for pollutants in our waterways. While a few governments have unenforceable guidelines for some pollutants, these are very few compared with the number and mixtures of chemicals actually flowing into Canada's natural waters.
— Kai Millyard in *Probe Post*, Fall, 1986

According to a 1989 Decima poll, 44% of Canadians believe that their tap water will not be drinkable by the year 2000. And considering that dioxin has already been found in drinking water from Lake Ontario, we don't have to wait until 2001 to be *concerned* about the quality of our tap water.

Many Canadians are turning to bottled water. In 1987, Canadians spent $110 million on these products. However, bottled water isn't necessarily more pure, because there are no federal regulations or standards that govern its purity or safety. Health and Welfare requires only that a

Toxic Hotspots in the Great Lakes

The International Joint Commission identified 42 areas of concern and 11 pollutants of primary concern. These pollutants are polychlorinated biphenyls (PCBs), DDT and metabolites; dieldrin, toxaphene, dioxin (2,3,7,8-TCDD), benzofuran (2,3,7,8-TCDF), mirex, mercury, alkylated lead, benzo(a)pyrene and hexachlorobenzene.

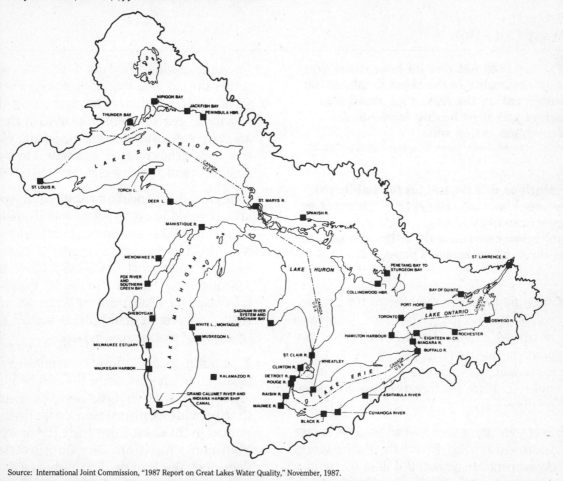

Source: International Joint Commission, "1987 Report on Great Lakes Water Quality," November, 1987.

substance be natural, free of coliform bacteria and properly labelled.

According to Pollution Probe, rather than buying bottled water or water purifiers, Canadians should be spending money in support of groups working for cleaner water. By attacking the root of the problem, we will ensure not only that our tap water will be safer to drink, but also that the sources of environmental contamination will be cleaned up.

WHAT CAN I DO?

The key is to not give up hope. Once you stop swimming in the river, drinking the water, eating the fish, it's a small step before you start buying masks and decontamination suits.
— Daniel Green, Société pour vaincre la pollution, *Globe and Mail*, August 18, 1989

Solutions will depend on the public will as much as technology; few industries or governments will spend their funds on pollution controls unless they are urged to do so by an aroused populace.
— Ron Reid in *Nature Canada*, Winter, 1989

• Become an active member of the aroused public! Be informed. Where does your town or city get its water supply? What is the condition of that water supply? Where does your waste water go when you pull the plug in the sink? Are there any threats to the groundwater in your area?

• Does your city or town have an adequate sewage treatment facility? Phone the Public Works department to find out. If it does not, write a letter of concern to the mayor or to your councillor and send a copy to the local paper.

• Do some "digging." Find out if there are companies in your area that are polluting waterways. (You could start by contacting the provincial environment ministry.) If there are, why not write to them, expressing your concerns? Send copies of your letters to local politicians and to the newspaper.

• Find out which environment group in your area is working on issues of water quality. Your provincial environment network will have this information. Support the group's efforts to ensure that all Canadians have safe drinking water. Pollution Probe, for example, is lobbying for a Safe Drinking Water Act with legally enforceable standards, to replace the "guidelines" that are now in place.

• Find out more about toxic contamination of local water supplies. Pollution Probe publishes a "Great Lakes Toxic Hotspots Poster" that provides information on pollution sources in the Great Lakes basin and areas of high contamination. The Conservation Council of New Brunswick publishes an illustrated directory, *Toxic Hotspots in the Maritimes*.

- The bleaching process used by many pulp and paper mills leads to the release of dioxins into waterways. There would be no market for chlorine-bleached white paper if consumers asked for non-chlorine bleached paper products. (See Chapter 11, "Garbage: Trim that Tonne," for information on where to buy such paper in Canada.)

- Take the initiative at a local level. Are there rivers or streams in need of clean-up? Try to get a local club involved and organize an event around a litter pick-up. In the summer of 1987 students cleaning up urban waterways in Ontario removed 751,871 kg of debris (including a tire that weighed 1,000 lbs and four stolen vehicles).

- Some B.C. communities have Storm Drain Marking programs. Volunteers mark a fish symbol near the storm drains to graphically remind the public that "down the drain" means into the local stream. Contact the regional office of the federal department of Fisheries and Oceans for information about volunteering.

- Don't overload the storm sewer system: drain your eavestroughs onto your lawn or into a barrel rather than into the sewers.

- If you live near one of the Great Lakes, get involved with the Remedial Action Plans. Contact Environment Canada or Ontario's Ministry of the Environment, or call the RAP toll-free line at 1-800-265-0248; find out what steps are being taken to clean up the lake. As well, contact the Ontario Ministry of the Environment about the MISA program. The organizers are inviting public participation.

The Great Festival of the Lakes

The Great Festival of the Lakes is an environmental awareness campaign initiated by the Society for Preservation of Wild Culture. The festival is participatory and celebratory:

"I have this theory that if you put two people beside a polluted river for long enough, then eventually they'll think of a scheme to clean it up.... Well, our scheme is called *The Great Festival of the Lakes*. It is based on the notion that if the lakes are to be brought back to life, then the Great Lakes people will have to be the ones to do it. After all the reports have revealed what's wrong, after all the statistics have been thrown up and thrown out, it is still up to the people who live here...

"The Great Festival of the Lakes aims to make us all more aware of water pollution, how it is caused and how it affects us, in a way that can at the same time rekindle our imagination and vision of the Great Lakes....

"Instead of meeting around the idea of polluted water, we'll focus on clean water....

"There is a dream for the lakes: *swimmable, drinkable, fishable*. People in laboratories or legislatures can't realize that dream for us.... When each of us, as individuals, assumes responsibility for where we live, then we'll be well on our way to making the lakes great again."

The Journal of Wild Culture, May, 1988

- Find out more about how you can participate or donate to The Great Festival of the Lakes; contact 158 Crawford Street, Toronto, Ontario M6J 2V4; (416) 588-8266.

- If your home is heated by oil that is stored in an outdoor tank, have the tank checked for leaks. Make sure that no oil is spilt when the tank is being filled or serviced. Check for rust before filling. The Conservation Council of New Brunswick publishes a booklet, *Preventing Petroleum Storage Tank Leaks: A Citizen's Guide*, that outlines what individuals can do. (See source list for address.) The Petroleum Association for Conservation of the Canadian Environment can provide technical information and assistance.

- Next time you throw something into the garbage, down the drain or into the sewer, do the water test. Ask yourself: Do I want to end up drinking these chemicals? See Chapter 7, "Hazardous Wastes and Toxic Substances," and Chapter 10, "Home: Getting Our Own Houses in Order," for more information on how to dispose of household hazardous waste and alternatives to chemicals in the home. See Chapter 15, "Transportation," for information on how to dispose of used motor oil from a do-it-yourself oil change.

- Wetlands are major sources of water for the aquifers that provide water to wells. See Chapter 9, "Wilderness," for information on preserving wetlands.

- Before altering the course of any river or stream, contact the provincial environment ministry. You may even be required to contact them by law.

- Water is a precious resource: make every drop count! See Chapter 13, "Energy Conservation in the Home," for suggestions on how to conserve water.

- Pesticides, herbicides and insecticides used in the garden may end up contaminating groundwater or becoming a part of the surface run-off feeding a lake or stream. See Chapter 16, "Yard and Garden," for alternatives to chemical weed and pest control.

• According to the Science Council of Canada, "pollution from agricultural sources is possibly the greatest and most intractable threat" to groundwater. One of the ways to reduce the chemicals used in agriculture is for consumers to demand and pay for produce grown without chemicals. See Chapter 8, "Agriculture," for a discussion of these issues and suggestions for ways to support organic food producers.

• Groundwater contamination is tied to many environmental issues including acid rain, garbage disposal, forestry practices, toxic spills, and chemicals in agriculture and gardening. Support groups that are trying to solve these problems.

• The Maritime Fishermen's Union, Local #4 has launched a campaign to alert fishers of the problem of plastic debris and litter in the marine environment. Write to the union for posters and bumper stickers. (See source list for address.)

• Find out more about the implications of free trade for Canada's water resources. Write to the Rawson Academy of Aquatic Science, Suite 404, 1 Nicholas Street, Ottawa, Ontario K1N 7B7 for a copy of *Water Is in the Deal* by Mel Clark and Don Gamble.

• Drinking water may be contaminated by the lead solder used by many plumbers and by old lead pipes in your house or in the city's water system. An excellent source of information on lead contamination and practical tips on identifying and rectifying lead problems is *The Citizen's Guide to Lead* by Kathy Cooper and Barbara Wallace (Toronto: NC Press, 1988). If you are worried about lead in your drinking water, there are two ways to reduce your exposure immediately. First, do not use water from the hot water tap for drinking or cooking. (Hot water is a more efficient solvent than cold water, and draws more lead from the pipes and solder.) Second, let your cold water tap run for at least a minute before using the water first thing in the morning. This will flush out water that has been sitting in the pipes overnight.

• When having plumbing repairs done, shop around for a plumber who uses lead-free solder and lead-free flux. If your home is an older one that has lead pipes, consider having them replaced. If you get your drinking water from a well in an area of high acidic precipitation, this is particularly important, as acidic water will draw greater quantities of lead from your pipes (see Chapter 1, "Acid Rain").

• If you are considering a purification system for your household drinking water, research the various options carefully in order to match the equipment with your particular contamination problem. This may involve having your tapwater tested, especially if you live in an agricultural area where pesticides are used and you get your water from a well. For information on where to get your water tested, contact your provincial ministry of the environment. Many private companies test water, and the Consumers' Association of Canada has a Water Analysis and Evaluation Service that tests for the presence of over 90 substances and provides suggestions on how to remove any harmful substances found. Contact CAC at Box 9300, Ottawa, Ontario K1G 3T9; (613) 723-0187.

• Once you have identified your contamination problem, there are a number of sources of information on which system best matches your needs. Contact your provincial ministry of the environment. Environment Ontario, for example, publishes a free booklet, *Information on the Use of Home Water Treatment Devices*. Alternatively, information is available from the Canadian Water Quality Association, a national trade association whose members are involved in the water quality business (472 Lee Avenue, Waterloo, Ontario N2K 1X9; (519) 885-3854). You can also contact *Canadian Consumer* magazine (Box 9300, Ottawa, Ontario K1G 3T9; (613) 723-0187) and order a copy of their October 1987 article "Giving Water the Treatment."

• If you do buy bottled spring water, write to the company and ask for the chemical analysis of the product. (The analysis is done routinely.)

You may also wish to check a comparative analysis done by *Canadian Consumer* magazine. The magazine looked at cost, taste and chemical content of the major bottled waters on the market. The results were published in the May 1987 issue of the magazine. Reprints of the article are available (see address above).

• The Environmental Hazards Management Institute has published a "Water 'Sense' Wheel," which lists symptoms or clues about water quality problems, probable causes and contaminants, health effects and treatment options. This handy reference wheel is available from EHMI, P.O. Box 932, 10 Newmarket Road, Durham, New Hampshire 03824; (603) 868-1496.

• To find out what standards the federal government has set for drinking water in Canada, order a copy of Health and Welfare's *Guidelines for Canadian Drinking Water Quality* (from the Canadian Government Publishing Centre, Supply and Services Canada, Ottawa, Ontario K1A 0S9). (Remember, though, that these standards are not legally enforceable.) You may wish also to order a copy of a critique of these guidelines, *The Myth of the Safe Drinking Water Standard*, published by the Conservation Council of New Brunswick (see source list for address).

Vanishing Forests:
Slash, Burn — and Gone

It has been said that we know more about some areas of the moon than we do about tropical rainforests.

— CATHERINE CAUFIELD, *IN THE RAINFOREST*

THE PROBLEM:

We are cutting down tropical rainforests on a massive scale. By doing so, we are destroying whole ecosystems, causing soil erosion, desertification and loss of species, threatening indigenous peoples, and contributing to the greenhouse effect.

THE SOLUTION:

Stop destroying the rainforests and start planting trees.

DEFINITION

Rainforests cover approximately 7% of the world's land surface, and stretch along the equator between the Tropic of Cancer and the Tropic of Capricorn. Characterised by high temperatures and heavy rainfall, tropical rainforests have been called "the lungs of the planet" because they play a role in converting carbon dioxide into oxygen. (However, rainforests also *consume* oxygen and *release* carbon dioxide as organic matter in the forest decomposes.)

Tropical rainforests regulate the world's water cycle, storing rainfall and slowly releasing moisture into the air. Without the moist forest cover, the soil would become dry, hard and easily eroded.

At least half (and some scientists estimate as much as two-thirds) of all species on the planet are found in the tropical rainforests. Many small areas of forest contain species that exist nowhere else, so when the forest is cut down or burned, some species are lost forever.

The biological diversity and richness of a rainforest ecosystem is almost impossible to imagine. One hectare (destroyed every three seconds) may contain thousands of species of plants, animals and insects. A study in Peru found 41,000 different insect species (which included 12,000 different types of beetles) within one hectare of rainforest.

CAUSES

There are three main causes of tropical deforestation: logging for timber; clearance for crops or cattle ranching; and resource development. Although these activities are carried out to different degrees in different countries, in each case the incentive for destroying the rainforest is a complex mix of economic, political and military agendas: developing countries need money to pay back massive foreign debts, and governments and the military need populated regions to protect sovereignty.

Logging

Tropical hardwoods — such as teak, mahogany, ebony and rosewood — are major exports from countries such as Malaysia. The wood is used for a variety of products from expensive furniture, to veneer on television sets, to cheap shipping crates, to chopsticks. (Some of the timber that is logged is used domestically to provide fuel for heat and power. Most, however, is exported to developed countries, primarily Japan.)

In 1987, Canadians imported over $90 million worth of tropical timber, in the form of veneer sheets, plywood and fibreboard.

The World's Rainforests

Rainforests cover 2% of the earth's surface (7% of the land mass). They originally covered at least twice that area.

Source: © 1988 Rainforest Action Network

Natural Distribution of Tropical Rainforests

	Central & South America	Africa & Madagascar	South & Southeast Asia
Original area TRF (square kilometres)	8.5 million	3.8 million	3.6 million
Current area TRF	5.4 million	1.8 million	2.0 million
Projected area TRF by the year 2000	3.3 million	1.2 million	0.7 million
Leading causes of deforestation	Cattle raising; forest farming; fuelwood (Central America)	Forest farming; logging; fuelwood (Madagascar)	Logging; forest farming; fuelwood (Indonesia)

Source: Rainforest Action Network

Farming and Cattle Ranching

Rainforests are also cleared to provide land for farming or cattle ranching. In some countries the act of clearing the land confers legal title or ownership on the person doing the clearing: moving into the rainforest and clearing land thus becomes one way for the landless to own property in many poor countries. However, statistics reveal just who is benefitting from land speculation: 93% of the arable land in Latin America is owned by 7% of the landowners.

Some governments support and encourage migration to rainforest areas; not only does such migration reduce population pressures on the cities, but it also ensures national sovereignty in unprotected or undefended frontier territories.

Once the land is cleared of trees, crops may be planted. However, rainforests typically have very shallow soil, not suited to agriculture, and can be cultivated for only 2 or 3 years on average.

Cleared rainforest land is also used for cattle ranching, which provides cheap beef to developed countries. Very little beef is distributed for domestic consumption: in 1978 the average Costa Rican consumed 12.5 kg of beef; the average North American pet cat consumed more. Since 1960 more than one-quarter of all forests in Central America have been destroyed in order to raise cattle, 90% of which went to the U.S., for use by fast-food chains and pet-food companies.

Most U.S. fast-food companies deny using rainforest beef. However, once beef is imported into the States (and rainforest beef *is* imported), it is inspected and stamped with its U.S. grade. When it is sold, it is impossible to track its country of origin.

Canada imports virtually no rainforest beef. However, it does import some tinned meat goods (such as corned beef) from Central American countries.

Hamburgers that Taste Like Sawdust

Cattle raised in Central America cost approximately one-quarter the price of North American cows. American fast-food chains have, over the years, fuelled rainforest destruction.

One hectare of rainforest weighs approximately 800 tons. When cleared, it will allow for the production of approximately 200 kg of beef — or 1,600 hamburgers. In other words, 6.25 m^2 or about half a ton of rainforest is destroyed per burger.

Source: Chris Uhl in *Bio Science*, Fall, 1988

Resource Development

Particularly in the Amazon, and again to ease massive debts and as part of a political program of industrialization, the government is sponsoring hydroelectric projects that flood whole regions of rainforest. The electricity produced by such projects is used to ease dependence on foreign sources and to power industrial development.

EFFECTS

According to the Worldwatch Institute, 11 million hectares (just under the combined size of Nova Scotia and New Brunswick) of tropical forest are cleared globally every year. (If one includes all trees that are logged or lost — not just tropical rainforest — an area twice the size of Prince Edward Island is cleared every month.) Translated into a more comprehensible scale, the destruction of rainforests is somewhere between 20 and 40 hectares every minute of every day.

If the current rate of clearing continues, we have only 10 to 50 years left before all tropical rainforests will be destroyed.

The True Cost of a Teak Table

Teak, which takes from 50 to 100 years to reach a harvestable size, grows only in tropical forests. On average, there is one teak tree per half-hectare of forest, interspersed with other tropical trees.

Before that tree is harvested, a logging road must be built to reach the stand. The road will destroy all trees in its path and open up the rainforest to other kinds of development. When the tree is harvested, all of the surrounding trees, which are connected by a thick and tangled web of the forest canopy, may be ripped down with it, destroying a compact and thriving ecosystem. The half-hectare in which the teak tree stands contains thousands of species of plants, animals and insects, many of them found only in that one area.

Source: Tovah Martin in *Harrowsmith*, September/October, 1988

Species Extinction

The health and lives of all people are endangered by this extinction.
— Steven Price, World Wildlife Fund in *NOW*, April 13, 1989

Although tropical rainforests contain from half to two-thirds of all living species on earth, most species have not yet been catalogued, much less studied. Under 1% of plants have been examined for possible medical uses, although one-quarter of prescription drugs in North America have active ingredients found in tropical plants. Approximately 10% of all plants identified by the U.S. National Cancer Institute as having anti-cancer properties are found only in rain-forests. Extrapolating from current findings, scientists have estimated that up to 40% of tropical species may have medical applications as yet unknown.

Many crops that are now found on grocery store shelves originated in tropical rainforests: rice, coffee, tea, bananas, cashews, cocoa, peanuts and pineapples, for example.

Present estimates suggest that from 1 to 24 species become extinct every day. As rainforest destruction continues, this number will rise. It may take under 100 years to lose half of the species on earth if current practices continue. The effects on the world's ecosystems are impossible to predict.

Global Warming

We all have a stake in the future of this unique ecosystem.
— David Suzuki, *Globe and Mail*

As trees are cut down and burned, they release all of their stored carbon into the atmosphere. Moreover, they are no longer available to convert carbon dioxide into oxygen. This leads to increased amounts of carbon dioxide in the atmosphere, a major cause of global warming. (See Chapter 2, "The Greenhouse Effect.")

Flooding, Soil Erosion and Desertification

Rainforests are like sponges: they capture, store and recycle rain. In the Amazon Basin, at least half of the rain that falls has been recycled from the forest. As the trees are destroyed, the rain is no longer absorbed by the forest canopy. Instead, it lands directly on the soil, causing flooding and washing away soil. (45 tons of soil per acre are washed away by tropical storms every year.)

When there are no trees to absorb and release rainwater, the soil becomes dry. The shallow soil, no longer fertilized by fallen debris from the trees above, becomes barren. In a process called desertification, once rich and alive rainforests end up as parched deserts.

Indigenous Peoples

Keep your money. You can print money, but you can't print land. We want our land.
— The Penan people of Sarawak responding to the bribes of loggers, quoted by Eric Hansen in *Stranger in the Forest*

Rainforests across the globe are home to many tribes. When governments decide to encourage clearing, they have to resettle the indigenous peoples. The basic existence of whole cultures is being destroyed along with the forests. In Brazil alone, approximately 220,000 Indians in 170 tribes are threatened.

According to Amnesty International, in 1985 222 rural people were killed in land struggles in the Amazon.

SOLUTIONS

The best way to change an institution is to force it to abide by its own rules.
— Saul Alinsky, quoted in R.J.A. Goodland, *How to Save Tropical Forests*

The bank will not assist development projects that knowingly involve encroachment on traditional territories.
— World Bank, *Tribal Peoples Policy*

The World Bank and other development banks lend over $26 billion a year to Third World countries for development projects. Canada contributed $2.8 billion in aid in 1988/89. Development projects that lead to the destruction of rainforests are coming under increasing criticism from environment groups. In 1989 a US$500 million World Bank loan to Brazil to help finance the construction of hydroelectric dams (which would have flooded rainforest) was stalled and then cancelled because of the negative environmental impact.

This decision was a mark of the success of an international network of environment groups, including the Canadian group Probe International, that has been attempting to reform agencies like the World Bank and to make their lending practices conform to environmental goals.

Other environment groups are calling for "debt-for-nature" swaps, through which the foreign debts of Third World countries (over $1 trillion owed in 1988) would be exchanged for protection of rainforests.

Some groups are taking other forms of direct action. In 1987 the World Wildlife Fund bought 20,000 acres (about 8,100 hectares) of rainforest in Costa Rica to add to the Monteverde Nature Reserve. Canadians, donating $25 an acre, contributed a total of half a million dollars in under 2 years. The World Wildlife Fund has expanded this program: each donation goes towards protecting rainforest already designated for preservation.

WHAT CAN I DO?

We're the last generation on earth that will have a chance to save the tropical rainforests.
— Randy Hayes, Rainforest Action Network in *Toronto Star*, December 4, 1988

• Instead of buying products made with tropical hardwoods — such as teak, mahogany, ebony and rosewood — buy products made with domestic woods such as pine, maple or cherry. Ask in furniture shops where the wood comes from.

• If you support Third World aid projects, be an educated donor. Ask questions before you give, and make sure that your donations are not funding destructive practices such as the flooding of rainforests and the relocation of indigenous peoples.

- Let others know about your concern for the tropical rainforests. Discuss the issues with people or professional associations whose work may in some way be related to the rainforests (for example, carpenters and most pharmacists). Encourage professional associations to develop a code of conduct with respect to rainforest products, as the American Institute of Architects did in 1989.

- Ask your financial institution about its policies for lending money to developing countries. Are projects screened for their environmental impact? Is financing given only to those projects that do not harm the environment? The World Bank now has an environment department; why should the Bank of Montreal or the Bank of Commerce, for example, not follow suit?

- Write to the federal finance minister (who represents Canada at the World Bank) and to the Canadian International Development Agency (CIDA) and let them know that you want your tax dollars to go to environmentally sound development. Letters *do* make a difference. (See source list for addresses.)

- Donate to the World Wildlife Fund's "Guardian of the Rainforest" campaign; you will be protecting an acre of rainforest from logging, poaching or clearing. (See source list for address.)

- Support groups, such as Probe International, that are working to save the rainforests. Your dollars help these groups to continue their work, and to lobby businesses, banks and government to save the rainforest.

- Take part in Rainforest Action Week, held every year in the fall. Contact Probe International to find out how you can help in your community.

- Canada's own temperate rainforests are increasingly under threat from unsustainable logging. See Chapter 9, "Wilderness," for a discussion of the issues and what you can do.

- Plant trees. According to the Worldwatch Institute, at least 130 million hectares of trees have to be planted annually to offset the rate of global deforestation.

- Friends of the Earth has produced a Tropical Rainforest Education Kit, aimed at high school students in grades 11 to 13. The kit includes a slide show and teacher's guide and is available to educators. (See source list.)

Garbage:
Our Gross National Product

Throw away the whole notion of garbage, if anything has to be thrown away.

— GORDON PERKS, GREENPEACE

THE PROBLEM:

We are producing too much garbage, all of which represents wasted resources and wasted energy.

THE SOLUTION:

Reduce the production of garbage at source.

Waste and affluence seem to go hand in hand. The better off we are as a nation, the more secure our natural resources, the more we waste. "Throw away" seems to be a measure of prosperity.

DEFINITION

If the idea of garbage isn't exactly being glamorized, the language of garbage is being sanitized: it isn't just garbage anymore, the stuff that conveniently used to go away. Instead, it's "the waste stream," or "post-consumer product." Dumps are now called landfill sites, where waste is put into "natural attenuation entombment." In the process of redefining the terms, the focus has shifted away from the problem of garbage production, to the question of waste management.

But many environmentalists offer a different way of looking at garbage — as a misplaced resource, or the sign of an inefficient system. Garbage thus becomes "used" material, composed of products that we bring into the economy and take out when all of the possibilities for their use are exhausted. In this new equation, the energy, labour and capital invested in producing a product is taken into account before we label an item garbage — or, literally, useless.

The connection is borne out by statistics: with just 8% of the world's population, North Americans produce 50% of the world's garbage.

CAUSES

There is nothing we do that does not generate waste. Even thinking produces waste, because your body consumes food in the process.
— B.C. Ministry of Environment, *Garbage is Resource Full*

On average, each Canadian produces 1.8 to 2 kg of household garbage every day, or from two-thirds to a tonne per person per year. According to Environment Canada, we are the most wasteful country on earth. (In the United States, per capita production of garbage is 1.6 kg daily; in Switzerland, 1.1 kg; and in Norway, .77 kg.) In total, 16 to 20 million tonnes of garbage is produced by Canadians every year.

Approximately one-third of the household garbage we produce is composed of paper; another third is organic waste (food scraps and yard refuse); and the final third is glass, metal, plastic, textiles and wood.

However, residential waste makes up just one-third to one-half of the total waste stream; the rest is produced in manufacturing and industrial processes that provide us with the goods we buy and the services we demand. If this waste is added in, Canadians produce 35 to 40 million tonnes of solid garbage every year.

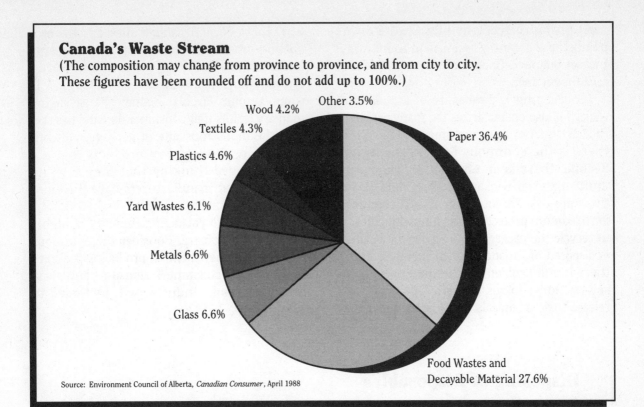

Canada's Waste Stream
(The composition may change from province to province, and from city to city.
These figures have been rounded off and do not add up to 100%.)

Other 3.5%

Wood 4.2%

Textiles 4.3%

Plastics 4.6%

Yard Wastes 6.1%

Metals 6.6%

Glass 6.6%

Paper 36.4%

Food Wastes and
Decayable Material 27.6%

Source: Environment Council of Alberta, *Canadian Consumer*, April 1988

Packaging: "Conspicuous Containerism"

Packaging was not created to increase garbage but was created in response to social needs and the demands of the marketplace. Packaging developers do not go to work and say "How can I create more garbage today?" There is nothing complex about the packaging issue; if you won't buy the package, it won't survive in the marketplace.

— Alan Robinson, Packaging Association of Canada, *Strategies for Waste Reduction,* June 1988

Packaging is a $12 billion-a-year industry in Canada, employing approximately 60,000 people in 14,000 companies. Packaging is used to keep a product fresh, pure, free from contamination and breakage; in other words, to protect a product completely from the time that it is produced, through the transportation process, to the time that it is bought by the consumer.

Packaging also serves an information function, which is regulated by government: in Canada, a package must include a bilingual label listing the contents, the nature of the product, the company's name and address, and the net quantity. Undeniably, the package also *sells* the product.

If packaging is a measure of a consumer society, it also characterizes the many problems that arise from our consumer habits. First, there is the enormous bulk of packaging. Second, there is an offshoot problem with multi-material packaging. The more layers there are of different materials, all combined for maximum protection, the more difficult it is to recycle the package. As a result, the package is disposed of in landfill or incinerated. Third, there is the problem of the materials themselves. Some foams contain CFCs; plastics release toxic chemicals when burned and they don't break down in landfill sites; and the production process for some packaging is energy intensive.

The whole issue of excess packaging is wrapped up in circular blame. The packaging industry claims that consumer demand has created the monstrous pile of garbage, yet consumers continue to buy products that are over-packaged thinking that they have no choice — that manufacturers have produced the excess packaging problem.

However, the packaging industry is highly consumer-responsive. Consider the enormous amount of money spent on producing packages that "sell." If consumers refuse to buy over-packaged goods, industry will be forced to adapt.

Disposing of Disposables

Every year, Americans throw away 16 billion disposable diapers, 1.6 billion pens, 2 billion razors and blades, 220 million tires, and enough aluminum to rebuild the entire U.S. commercial airline fleet every three months.

Source: John Langone in *TIME*, January 2, 1989

Take-Out Trouble

According to the Polystyrene Packaging Council, polystyrene (the plastic used to make take-out cups, fast-food containers and other disposable packaging) accounts for one-quarter of 1% (by weight) of the solid waste in North American landfill sites.

In 1986, the polystyrene industry in Canada produced 188,000 tonnes of polystyrene; approximately one-quarter of this total went to make disposable products and packaging.

In North America, approximately 3,000 tonnes of polystyrene (enough to make 900 million take-out coffee cups) ends up in garbage cans every day. If loosely packed, these cups would fill 100 75-storey office towers. Every day.

Source: *Globe and Mail*, February 6, 1989, and The Society of Plastics Industries

EFFECTS

Canadian taxpayers spend more than $1.5 billion a year on waste management. Most of the garbage produced in Canada is sent to landfill sites; a small portion is incinerated. Both of these options are not really waste disposal, but rather volume-reduction techniques.

When garbage is incinerated, part is left in the form of ash. When garbage is dumped in landfill sites, it is basically being stored and reduced by compaction, shredding, baling or decomposition. Both landfill and incineration have environmental price-tags.

Incineration is the burning of solid waste; the results are ashes and flue gases. After incineration, 10 to 20% by volume of garbage remains as bottom ash (which stays in the furnace) or fly ash (which is airborne). The ash then has to be disposed of in a landfill site.

One of the main problems with incineration is that, if the incinerator is not highly efficient, the emissions from the burning process and the resulting ashes may pose risks to human health and to the environment.

Because in most cases little is known about the exact composition of each load of garbage, there is no control over what gets burned. Toxic and hazardous materials may be going up the stack and into the air. (For example, a 1983 report from the federal Expert Advisory Committee on Dioxins concluded that the incineration of municipal garbage is the primary contributor of dioxin to the Canadian environment.) The resulting ash may also contain toxins or hazardous substances that are simply transported to landfill sites.

Although new landfill sites are much more efficient at containing and controlling wastes, many older sites — still in use — allow toxins and poisons to leach out. When rainwater lands on an uncapped and undrained site, it filters through the garbage, picking up chemicals, and either leaches down to the groundwater or becomes surface runoff. Thus, dangerous substances may leach out of ordinary garbage dumps in liquid form or escape into the atmosphere as gases.

Given the potential health hazards, the unsightliness, the odour, and the constant line of trucks, it is not surprising that many Canadians are fighting decisions to locate landfill sites within or close to their communities.

At the same time as landfill sites across the country are filling up, it is getting harder and harder to find new locations.

Canadian Waste Facts

- In Canada, an estimated 23 to 26 million tires are discarded annually. Most end up buried in landfill sites, where they are a fire hazard. However, used tires have tremendous recycling potential; they can be used to make car bumpers, carpet underlay, asphalt for roads and driveways, car and truck splash guards, shoe soles and heels.

- Every tonne of newspapers recycled saves approximately 17 to 19 trees. Moreover, much less energy is needed to recycle paper than to process raw wood fibre.

- According to Colin Isaacs, former executive director of Pollution Probe, if everyone in Ontario (9 million people) recycled their newspapers, it would save 16,000 trees every weekday.

- The total amount of paper wasted by Canadians every year equals 80 million trees.

- For every tonne of steel cans recycled, more than a tonne and a half of iron ore is saved, along with the energy equivalent to almost three barrels of oil.

- Over seventy percent less energy is needed to produce aluminum from recycled cans than from raw materials.

- Ninety-eight percent of used motor oil can be reclaimed and reused through recycling.

- If all of the garbage produced by one person each year were put into a can, the lid would be at the top of a stack 60 metres high.

SOLUTIONS

To win our war on waste, we will involve the householder, the office worker, the student, the banker and the baker.
— James Bradley, Ontario's Minister of the Environment, *Globe and Mail*, March 11, 1989

Waste disposal in Canada is the responsibility of the provinces. Each province regulates the manner in which regional or municipal governments dispose of waste, and each province has different regulations. Prince Edward Island, for example, is the only province to prohibit the use of all non-refillable pop bottles. Manitoba, on the other hand, has added an Environmental Protection Tax to all non-deposit alcoholic beverage containers.

Along with the different provincial initiatives, each municipality offers different services. Curbside "Blue Box" recycling is a relatively recent, but rapidly expanding, form of waste management. Some municipalities have even introduced schemes to encourage residents to make their own compost.

In April 1989, the federal and provincial governments pledged to reduce Canada's garbage by 50% by the year 2000.

Ultimately, however, the reponsibility for garbage rests with each individual. The garbage crisis begins in the homes of all Canadians — and includes the industrial wastes produced in the manufacturing of products we buy — and doesn't end when we take our cans out to the curb or our bags to the dump.

Motto of the consumer society: Throw it away.

Motto of the conserver society: Where is away?

The 4 Rs
The 4 Rs — reduce, reuse, recycle, recover — have been the rallying cry of those people trying to find solutions to the garbage crisis. To these, several other Rs may be added — reject, refuse and repair, for example. The major appeal of the 4-R system is that it attacks the root of the problem: overproduction designed

for overconsumption, leading to overwastage. Each of the Rs lowers the amount of waste that has to be managed by options such as landfilling and incineration.

Reduce
Materials can be kept out of the waste stream in the first place. This requires changes in

consumer habits — not buying products that are overpackaged, and substituting reusable products for disposables, for example. It also requires major and complex fundamental changes: consuming less; producing *durable* goods, even if that means people won't be buying a newer model every year; packaging in environmentally low impact materials; and doing away with the whole notion of disposables.

Reuse

It is possible to reuse materials that have served their primary purpose. These may include products that are specifically designed for reuse (such as refillable beverage containers) or those that may be reused for completely different purposes. As a result, fewer materials will enter the waste stream *and* non-renewable resources will be conserved.

Canadian Waste Materials Exchange: One Company's Garbage is Another Company's Raw Material

> "Waste Product Feels Unwanted, — Seeks Mutually Satisfying Relationship"
>
> Source: Canadian Waste Materials Exchange

The volume of waste by-products from industrial processes presents both a challenge and an opportunity to manufacturers. The challenge is to reduce the amount of waste produced and to recycle materials within the company; the opportunity is to exchange waste products with potential users. Finding the potential user is the service offered by the Canadian Waste Materials Exchange.

The CWME publishes a bi-monthly bulletin that lists industrial wastes being offered or sought for re-use by companies across Canada. With 11 categories of materials, the exchange is responsible for the transfer of approximately 343,000 tonnes of materials every year.

The "Wastes Available" ads make for interesting, if bizarre reading: 500 lbs of oyster shells per week; 0.5 tonnes of spent fluorescent lamps per week; 20 tons of titanium dioxide sludge per year; 20 sunken ships off the coast of Newfoundland and Nova Scotia.

The Canadian Waste Materials Exchange can be reached at (416) 822-4111.

Recycle

Waste materials are collected and used in the manufacture of new products. Over 70% of all residential waste can be recycled, reducing the amount of garbage we throw away, conserving resources and saving energy. However, Canadians recycle, on average, just 2% of municipal garbage a year, giving us one of the lowest recycling rates among developed countries.

Along with the many advantages of recycling, there is one very positive but intangible benefit: while separating recyclables from non-recyclables, we are forced to *think* about the garbage we produce.

Recover

Both materials and energy can be extracted from waste. Composting is a form of recovery, in that compostable materials are separated and retrieved, or recovered and diverted from landfill. Energy-from-waste schemes are also a form of recovery: for example, it may be possible to recover energy from the half a million tonnes of sewage sludge produced in Canada each year.

Based on the Möbius loop, this recycling symbol signifies the use and re-use of materials. The three arrows stand for the different substances that can be recycled: solids, liquids and gases.

Source: Environment Canada

WHAT CAN I DO?

Take garbage personally. Think clean thoughts, and then transform them into less wasteful activities.

— *Globe and Mail, Report on Business*, August 1989

• Turn off the waste tap by using the 4 Rs.

Reduce

Garbage is a consumer issue. To reduce what we throw out, we have to reduce what we take home on our shopping trips. A good way to start is to consider the implications of a purchase *before* buying a product. Some general questions to ask are:

• Is the product overpackaged? (Consider how much packaging goes into one take-out dinner from a fast-food restaurant, for example.)

• Are you buying a disposable when there are alternatives? Disposable diapers, plates, utensils, cups, lighters, pens, razors, even cameras: all can be replaced with durable items that won't pile up in landfill sites.

• Is the product built to last? Although long-lasting products may cost more initially, they are often cost-effective. Remember environmental accounting when calculating your budget and buy durables.

• Are you buying on impulse, swayed by a packaging "hard sell," or are you buying out of need?

Reuse

There's lots of room for creativity in this category and no limit to the number of ways that materials can be reused.

• Once you're finished with an item, think of others who may be able to use it and give your cast-offs a new life. Many charities, such as Goodwill or the Salvation Army, accept used furniture and appliances. Some will even pick them up from your home for free. Magazines and books could go to libraries, hospitals, women's centres, seniors' homes or halfway houses. The CNIB accepts old eyeglasses. Demolition companies, junk shops, even antique stores, may take old windows and doors.

• Buy returnable beverage containers.

• Reuse envelopes. You can order stickers to place over the old address from the following sources: Permacycle, Box 4321, Quesnel, British Columbia V2J 3J3; Harringtons, R.R. #2, Galena Bay, Nakusp, British Columbia V0G 1R0; Saskatchewan Environmental Society, P.O. Box 1372, Saskatoon, Saskatchewan S7K 3N9.

• Reuse all plastic bags. Take your own bags to the grocery store, for example. For some bags (e.g., frozen vegetable packages) you will have to wash the bag and then turn it inside-out to dry on the dishrack.

Recycle

You can find out what is being done in your community by phoning the Public Works Department. Is there a curbside recycling program? If not, are there recycling bins or depots where you can take your recyclables?

- If there is no recycling, write letters to the mayor and to your councillor in support of setting up a program. Send a copy of the letter to the newspaper. Find out if there are any environment groups trying to set up a recycling system in your community.

- If there is recycling, make sure that you're putting the right materials in the Blue Box. Phone the Public Works department for a complete list of what your municipality accepts for recycling and what it doesn't. Alternatively, you could phone your provincial recycling council; see source list for addresses.

- Help set up a recycling program for fine paper and pop cans in your office. Contact your provincial recycling council for information on how to go about doing this.

- If you change the motor oil in your car, drop off the used oil for recycling at a participating garage. (See Chapter 15, "Transportation.")

- Contact your provincial recycling council for ways that you can get involved in the annual Recycling Week activities.

- While much attention is focussed on the front end of recycling (i.e., collecting materials), the end of the process is equally important. Once we've collected all of our newspapers and put them out for recycling, the next step is to *buy* recycled products. Look for the recycling symbol on all products.

- If there isn't a source of recycled paper in your community, you can order a wide variety of paper products (from 100% recycled, non-chlorine bleached fine paper to envelopes, to computer paper) from a number of companies in Canada. (See source list for addresses.) The Paper Source also sells a stamp so you can mark your envelopes "Recycled Paper" and spread the word.

Buyer Beware

Not all recycled paper products are created equal. Although the phrase "This product contains recycled fibre" sounds good, it may in fact signal that paper mill waste (e.g., scraps and cuttings from the ends of paper rolls), which has always been re-used within the paper-making process, is being passed off as post-consumer paper. Read the label carefully.

Post-consumer waste: High grade waste paper (such as office waste) that has been reclaimed and recycled.

Secondary Fibre: Waste paper generated at the paper mill and recycled.

Most recycled paper is made from a combination of the two. Look for 100% recycled, non-chlorine bleached paper.

• The Western Canada Wilderness Committee has produced garbage can stickers with the message "I'd Rather Curbside Recycle." (See source list.)

Recover

Composting is a form of material recovery that is easy for individuals to undertake. Almost all food scraps (except meat and oil, which will attract animals) can be put into a compost heap or bin. You can buy compost bins at most garden centres, or you can start a pile in the corner of the yard. (See Chapter 11, "Garbage: Trim that Tonne," for more information about how to start a compost heap.)

• Many municipalities are involving the public in decisions about waste management, providing an opportunity for you to voice your support for the 4 Rs. For information on how to get involved, phone your provincial recycling council or provincial environment network and ask what groups in your area are working on waste management issues and how you can get involved in municipal decision making.

• What is in your garbage? Where does it go? How long before the current landfill site is full? Where will the next one go? (In whose back yard?) One visit to the dump might reveal just how much of a garbage problem your municipality has. Tours are often available.

• Don't litter.

• Organize a litter clean-up in your neighbourhood. All you need is a garbage bag (or, most likely, bags) and willing workers.

• Hazardous materials, which include many familiar household products, should not be included in your regular garbage. This whole area is covered in more depth in the next chapter, "Hazardous Wastes and Toxic Substances" and in Chapter 10, "Home: Getting Our Own Houses in Order."

(See Chapter 11, "Garbage: Trim That Tonne," for more suggestions.)

Hazardous Wastes and Toxic Substances

Households, with an average annual output of nine gallons of toxic waste each, make up the largest single class of hazardous waste generators in Canada.

— SARAH WINTERTON, *PROBE POST*, SUMMER 1987

THE PROBLEM:

Hazardous wastes and toxic substances are being released into the air, soil and water.

THE SOLUTION:

Keep hazardous wastes and toxic substances from being released indiscriminately and untreated into the environment.

When we think of hazardous wastes and toxic chemicals, we often point to big industries or chemical manufacturers as being responsible not only for the production and use of such substances, but also for their disposal. But we should not forget our own backyards, garages, kitchens, bathrooms, basements and cupboards.

Such common household products as cleaners, detergents, paints, barbecue starter fluids, and even some cosmetics are in fact hazardous substances. If they are not handled with care, stored properly and disposed of safely, they can contaminate the air, soil and water. For many of these products, however, safe alternatives do exist and can be easily substituted.

DEFINITION

To many people, synthetic chemicals are mysterious, somewhat suspect substances. We depend on experts to evaluate them, governments to license them and industries to dispose of them. We tend to take their safety for granted.

There are approximately 100,000 chemicals in commercial use worldwide, and 1,000 new ones entering the market every year. In Canada, under the Canadian Environmental Protection Act (CEPA), new chemicals have to go through extensive testing before they can be registered for use. The assessment requires the following information: chemical and toxicity data, effects on human health, effects on animal and plant life, toxic effects on the ecosystem, long- and short-term exposure data, and information on the routes of exposure.

The information on any new synthetic chemical (i.e., the results of the assessment and recommended controls) is compiled into a report, which is made public.

However, the legislation refers to *new* substances — those developed after 1988. Before the passage of CEPA, Canadian industries could introduce a new chemical without informing Environment Canada and without releasing toxicity information to Health and Welfare. The thousands of chemicals developed before 1988 were assumed safe until proven otherwise! Unfortunately, the naivety of this assumption has been demonstrated over and over again.

According to the U.S. National Research Council, there is no toxicity information whatsoever on 4 out of 5 "chemicals in commerce." For the remaining 20%, there is only minimum toxicity information, and the NRC found that even this information was derived, in some cases, from problematic and incomplete testing. Information on chronic toxicity and effects on reproductive/developmental biology, in particular, was lacking.

The situation in Canada is similar to that in the United States. However, to deal with the enormous backlog of chemicals in use for which no formal regulations, toxicity data or safety requirements are in place, the federal government (with an expert advisory panel) has compiled a Priority Substances List. At present, the list includes 42 substances (such as dioxins and furans) that have been given the highest priority for health and environment impact assessment. Considering the number of chemicals in commercial use worldwide (approximately 100,000), the task of assessing the toxicity and drawing up guidelines for the safe handling and disposal of all chemicals could take decades. And until such work is carried out, we will continue to take the safety of chemicals for granted.

"Ever ask a rat if it suffers nightmares or has a headache? No laboratory experiments on animals can predict the toxic effects on humans of long-term exposure to small amounts of chemicals."

— Ross Hume Hall, chair of the expert committee that drew up the list of priority substances under the Canadian Environmental Protection Act, in *Probe Post*, Spring 1987

According to Environment Canada, hazardous wastes are "those wastes which, due to their nature or quantity, are potentially hazardous to human health or the environment and which require special disposal techniques to eliminate or reduce the hazard." They may be explosive, flammable, volatile, corrosive, radioactive, toxic or pathological wastes.

A substance may be hazardous for a number of reasons: because of its chemical composition (i.e., what it's made of); because of its quantity (i.e., hazardous only in large amounts); because of its persistence in the environment (i.e., it doesn't break down into benign components); or because of its potential to mix with other chemicals to create even more toxic substances.

The danger from hazardous substances may be immediately apparent or long term.

Hazardous Products Symbols		Danger	Warning	Caution
Toxic or Poisonous (materials such as pesticides, cleaning fluids or rat poison that are poisonous or lethal to animals, plants and humans)				
Flammable (liquids that can ignite, such as gasoline, barbecue lighter fluid or solvents)				
Reactive or Explosive (materials such as ammonia, bleach and pool chemicals that can create an explosion or release deadly vapours when mixed)				
Corrosive (substances such as battery acid or drain cleaner that eat away at materials)				

Source: Consumer and Corporate Affairs Canada

Chemicals in Perspective

Everything in the physical world is made of chemicals: the earth, air, food, plants, animals, cars, houses, and so on. Some chemicals are synthetic; that is, they do not exist naturally. All chemicals can be poisonous to humans if the amount being inhaled, ingested or absorbed is high enough.

Toxicity: A measure of the poisoning strength of a chemical, its capacity to do harm or injury.

Hazard: The likelihood that a chemical will cause poisoning, depending on its strength, the amount and the manner in which it is used.

A chemical that is not highly toxic may present a significant hazard, just as a highly toxic chemical may present a low hazard, depending on the nature and method of use.

Factors that influence the degree of poisoning caused to humans by chemicals include route of entry into the body; amount or dose entering the body; toxicity of the chemical; removal from the body; individual biological variation between people.

It is also important to note that chemicals rarely act in isolation. By a process called mutagenicity, one chemical can greatly increase the negative effects of another. For example, the carcinogenicity of plutonium in water multiplies when chlorine is added.

CAUSES

It is estimated that over 6 million tonnes of hazardous wastes are produced each year in Canada. The major sources are grouped into 4 categories by Environment Canada:

- By-products of industrial manufacturing processes;
- Consumer products that are discarded or contaminated;
- Accidental spills from storage sites or transportation;
- Discarded products and residues from laboratories and institutions: for example, contaminated medical waste.

Along with these domestic sources, Canada also imports hazardous wastes from the United States for treatment here. A 1986 agreement, the Canada-USA Agreement on the Trans-boundary Movement of Hazardous Waste, guarantees virtual free trade in hazardous materials. In 1988, Canada imported 120,000 tonnes of hazardous waste from the U.S., 80,000 tonnes more than was sent there for disposal.

Disposing of hazardous wastes is the reponsibility of each province. The first step of any management plan is to identify the types and quantities of hazardous materials that are generated, or that have already been produced, disposed of or abandoned. The next is to ensure that a system is set up for the safe handling and disposal of such materials.

Although each province has set up different programs to achieve these goals, in 1989 the federal government offered the provinces $100 million over five years to clean up hazardous waste sites in Canada.

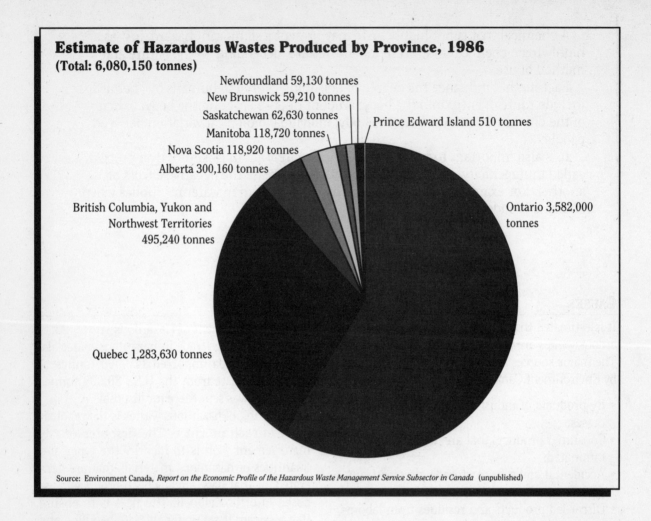

Estimate of Hazardous Wastes Produced by Province, 1986
(Total: 6,080,150 tonnes)

Newfoundland 59,130 tonnes
New Brunswick 59,210 tonnes
Saskatchewan 62,630 tonnes
Manitoba 118,720 tonnes
Nova Scotia 118,920 tonnes
Alberta 300,160 tonnes

Prince Edward Island 510 tonnes

British Columbia, Yukon and
Northwest Territories
495,240 tonnes

Ontario 3,582,000
tonnes

Quebec 1,283,630 tonnes

Source: Environment Canada, *Report on the Economic Profile of the Hazardous Waste Management Service Subsector in Canada* (unpublished)

Household Hazardous Wastes

The hazardous wastes generated in Canadian homes are much more difficult to monitor and regulate than industrial waste. The first step in dealing with the problem of household hazardous wastes is for individuals to recognize what materials are hazardous, and then seek safer alternatives. If no alternatives exist, then the next step is for individuals to dispose of hazardous wastes properly (see Chapter 11, "Garbage: Trim that Tonne").

Here is a list of some everyday hazards:

Solvents

furniture and floor polish

shoe polish

silver and metal polish

spot removers

moth balls

paint thinners

paint removers

art supplies

wood stains

toilet bowl cleaners

window cleaners

pool chemicals and chlorine

rug cleaners

laundry and stain removers

floor wax stripper

lye

batteries

Caustic or Corrosive Substances

drain openers or cleaners

oven cleaners

chlorine bleach

scouring powders

Pesticides and Herbicides

bug sprays

mosquito repellant

chemical fertilizers

flea collars

weed killers

We should realize too that, as consumers, we bear indirect responsibility for the production of hazardous materials. We use, and in many ways benefit from, the complex new substances that are developed every year for commercial purposes. From plastics to synthetic fibres to artificial "food" products, all are now produced and used in greater amounts than ever before.

We have grown used to the convenience, but we are just now starting to account for the true cost of the hazardous wastes produced by manufacturing processes. But we have already reached the point where there is nowhere on earth we can go to escape the toxic legacy of hazardous wastes.

"We live in the Arctic and we don't create any real pollution. The real threat is coming from outside, which is the industrial world."

— Mary Simon, president, Inuit Circumpolar Conference, *Globe and Mail*

Scientists have found chemical pollutants in Arctic animals and plants that could be threatening the health of Canada's Inuit. PCBs have been found in Arctic fish, seals, caribou, berries and molluscs, and DDT has been found in polar bears and other large mammals.

The chemicals do not originate in the Arctic, but are carried there by global air and water currents. From the water they are absorbed by fish and move up the food chain. Because the Inuit depend for their diet on animal fat (where the chemicals concentrate), they are particularly at risk from the toxins.

EFFECTS

U.S. industry is pouring more than 10 billion kilograms of toxic chemicals into the air, water and land each year, the Environmental Protection Agency disclosed yesterday.... The releases broke down this way: 4.4 billion kilograms of chemicals into streams and other bodies of water, 1.2 billion kilograms into the air, 108 billion kilograms into landfills, 1.45 billion kilograms injected deep into the ground for disposal, 860 million kilograms shipped to municipal waste-water treatment plants and 1.18 billion kilograms sent to off-site treatment and disposal facilities.... "The numbers are startling... unacceptably high and far beyond what we thought was occurring," Linda Fischer, assistant EPA administrator for policy and planning, said at a news conference.

— *Globe and Mail*, April 13, 1989

I talk about [smoking] all the time; how it kills 35,000 people a year in Canada, but what I think we don't understand is that the dangers from alcohol abuse and smoking pale in comparison to the dangers of pollution of our environment.

— Sandy Murray, president of the Alberta Medical Association

On March 24, 1989, when the *Exxon Valdez* oil tanker dumped over 40 million litres of oil into Prince William Sound in Alaska, public outrage was immediate and widespread. At least 10,000 people shredded and returned their credit cards to Exxon, protests and boycotts were held, and about 145 lawsuits (including a suit from the State of Alaska) have been launched against the company. The target of the protest was highly visible: the large corporation.

However, a disaster of this magnitude points to another target, one that was overshadowed by the vocal protest: our consumption of oil. To run the machinery on this planet, to feed consumer demands in developed countries, to support our lifestyles, we consume — worldwide — over 60 million barrels of crude oil a day. The *Exxon Valdez* spill represents under 1% (approximately 270,000 barrels) of this daily consumption.

While it is indeed necessary to monitor and strengthen transportation regulations and disaster response systems, environmentalists have long pointed out that accidental spills, explosions and related disasters are just a matter of time and chance if we continue to use such massive amounts of fuel. Only when we reduce our demands and shift to more benign sources of energy will the root of the problem be addressed. It is worth noting that as long ago as 1972, the U.S. government predicted that there would probably be more than 2 million litres of oil spilled each year along the west coast shipping route and that such oil spills were "inevitable."

"Exxon says it wants to build three small incinerators on land and a larger one on a barge to burn the solid waste left by the oil spill. The solid waste includes 20 tonnes of dead animals, 3,150 tonnes of oily pads, rags and clothes, 250 tonnes of heavily oiled logs and 3,650 tonnes of booms used to contain the oil spill on the water."

— *Globe and Mail*, May 3, 1989

SOLUTIONS

Keeping hazardous waste to an absolute minimum is an essential first step.
—Environment Canada

The 1987 act should be scrapped in favour of a radically different approach to the control of chemical pollution, an approach which can be stated in two words: *Don't pollute*. Ask the question, "How do chemicals get into the environ-ment?," and then set up legal procedures to block the sources of pollution.
— Ross Hume Hall in *Probe Post*, Spring 1987

The options available for keeping hazardous waste to an absolute minimum are the same as those that control all garbage production: the 4 Rs. By altering industrial processes and substituting safer materials, the amount of hazardous waste can be reduced; by reusing hazardous materials in the production process, wastes can be kept out of the waste stream; by recycling materials through "waste exchanges" with other industries, the useful life of hazardous materials can be extended; and by recovering either energy or materials from waste, the hazardous waste can be used more effectively.

Treatment of Hazardous Wastes

There are a number of waste treatment methods that can reduce the hazards associated with some materials. Most common is thermal destruction or incineration, a process that has to be properly designed and carefully operated to keep harmful gases from being created and released. Chemical treatment processes are also used either to reduce the toxicity of a substance or to transform hazardous wastes into materials that can be put into landfill. In biological treatment processes, certain micro-organisms feed on the waste.

However, all of these processes have some reduced form of residue that has to be disposed of in specially equipped landfill sites. Such sites have to be lined with materials that won't allow hazardous chemicals to leach into soil or groundwater, and they must be capped to ensure that excess rainwater does not cause runoff.

The simple fact is that, if we continue to produce hazardous wastes, we will have to dispose of them. The problem can be fully dealt with only at the source: the manufacturing processes that produce hazardous by-products and the consumer demands that power manufacturing.

WHAT CAN I DO?

- All synthetic products we buy, from plastics to synthetic fabrics, have an environmental cost in terms of hazardous wastes. We won't really get to the root of the problem until we curb consumption of synthetic products. Choose alternatives. For example, buy glass instead of plastics, natural fabrics as opposed to synthetic fibres.

- Use non-toxic alternatives to hazardous household materials (such as cleaning products). The basic ingredients of most non-toxic alternatives are just baking soda, vinegar and water, and they can easily be used at home. See Chapter 10, "Home: Getting Our Own Houses in Order," for non-toxic recipes.

- It's up to each of us to dispose of chemicals safely. Do not dispose of hazardous wastes in your regular garbage, down the drain or in the backyard. Call your provincial environment ministry, your Public Works department, or a local environment group to find out if your city conducts special waste collection days. If it does, save your hazardous wastes (in their original containers, with labels, if possible) and dispose of them on the special collection day.

- If your city or town does not have a hazardous waste disposal program, write letters to the mayor and councillors requesting that such a service be started.

Responsible Handling

"I consider myself a good driver, but I'm a bit nervous this trip. I've never carried hazardous waste before and I keep checking over my shoulder to see if the load's secure. I'm hauling a mixed cargo; waste ethylene, aliphatic hydrocarbons, a little malathion, and some used oil.

"I've joined a long line of vehicles inching forward through the heavy chain link gates of the depot. It seems to be taking a long time to check in and unload....

"The depot staff are dressed in white protective garments; the bulky moonsuits make their movements seem slow and awkward. The respirators and safety shields hide their faces and muffle their voices....

"I finally reach the head of the line. I turn off the engine, get out of the car, and reach into the back seat for the single cardboard box wedged there. I've got two cans of old paint, a half-full canister of bug killer and a plastic jug of used motor oil — household hazardous waste."

— William Glenn in *Living Safety*, Winter 1988/89

- Contact local environment groups working on hazardous waste issues and find out how you can help. Local groups are excellent sources of information if you are just starting to research the issues. For example, the Société pour vaincre la pollution has produced a colour-coded map of hazardous waste sites in Quebec, along with an explanatory brochure. (See source list for address.)

- Talk to people: your neighbour's hazardous waste may end up in your common water supply!

- If you have any questions about a chemical that you think might be hazardous or toxic, call the Canadian Chemical Producers' Association's Chemical Referral Centre: 1-800-267-6666. The centre also provides information about safe disposal.

- If you need toxicity or disposal information about any pesticide, herbicide, insecticide or agricultural chemical, call Agriculture Canada's National Pesticide Information Service at 1-800-267-6315.

- If you want information about any hazardous product that is used in the workplace, the Canadian Centre for Occupational Health and Safety has a toll-free number and an excellent data bank. Call 1-800-263-8276.

- Health and Welfare Canada operates the International Register of Potentially Toxic Chemicals, which will provide environmental, toxicological and legislative information on over 7,000 chemicals, free of charge. Call 1-800-267-3364.

- The U.S. National Library of Medicine and the Environmental Protection Agency have developed a data base called the Toxic Chemical Release Inventory, which will provide facts about the manufacturers of chemicals and where to get more information: (301) 496-6531.

- If you suspect that there has been a spill of hazardous materials, contact the National Environmental Emergency Service. Call collect, at (613) 997-3742. If the spill occurred while hazardous wastes were being transported, call the Canadian Transport Emergency Centre at (613) 996-6666. Provincial spill report numbers are:

  Yukon: (403) 667-7244
  Northwest Territories: (403) 920-8130
  British Columbia: 1-800-663-9453
  Saskatchewan: 1-800-667-7525
  Alberta: 1-800-222-6514
  Manitoba: (204) 944-4888
  Ontario: 1-800-268-6060
  Quebec: (514) 873-3453
  Maritimes: 1-800-565-1633
  Newfoundland: 1-800-563-2444

- If you are buying land, be aware of a new category of real estate: toxic or "hot" properties. As an unsuspecting buyer, you may end up with more than you bargained for if you don't look into the history of a property. (Quebec, in fact, keeps a registry of toxic properties in an effort to protect buyers.) Even if there is no evidence of industrial activity on or near the property, the area of town in which it stands may have once been an industrial section. Alternatively, a subdivision built on what is now the outskirts of town may have once been an unregulated dumping site. A simple check at City Hall should reveal the history of the property. Make your concerns known to the lawyer doing the title search and to your real estate agent. If one of the previous owners of the land was a numbered company, find out what business that company was in. This may seem unnecessarily cautious, but if you end up with contaminated property, you will most likely be the person responsible for the cost of cleaning it up.

- For information on how to handle and dispose of chemicals used in laboratories, schools or university research labs, see the *Hazardous Chemicals Information and Disposal Guide*. It is available from Terochem Laboratories Ltd., P.O. Box 8188, Station F, Edmonton, Alberta T6H 2P1.

Agriculture:
Biting the Land
That Feeds Us

In the summer after a heavy rainfall, we have tourists asking us why the river is chocolate-coloured, to which we reply that it is our soils that are being washed down the river.... They do not realize that they are seeing their next 30 to 40 years' food supply passing in front of them.

— JACQUES LAFORGE, NEW BRUNSWICK, IN *SOIL AT RISK*

THE PROBLEM:

Urban encroachment and modern farming practices are threatening the land that is the basis of food production.

THE SOLUTION:

Farmers have to adopt conservation agriculture methods; governments have to encourage and support conservation programs through economic and land-use policies; and consumers have to support local producers who use conservation practices.

In 1984, the Standing Senate Committee on Agriculture, Fisheries and Forestry studied the problem of soil degradation in Canada, consulting with farmers, environmental groups, agricultural organizations and government representatives. Their report, *Soil at Risk:* *Canada's Eroding Future*, came to the conclusion that "Canada is facing the most serious agricultural crisis in its history and unless action is taken quickly, this country will lose a major portion of its agricultural capability."

DEFINITION

From the top of the CN Tower in Toronto, you can see almost one-third of Canada's best (Class 1) agricultural land. But you can hardly see farmland at all; what you see is one urban centre after another, filled with buildings and connected by highways.

Although Canada is the world's second largest country, only 0.5% of the total land area, or 4.2 million hectares, is of Class 1 agricultural capability. Only about 11% of Canada's land base is capable of any form of agriculture; approximately 5% (an area the size of Sweden) is suitable for crop production.

Canada's Land Inventory: Agricultural Classification

Class 1: Agricultural land of the highest quality, with no physical limitations for crop production
$41,950 \text{ km}^2$

Class 2: Land capable of sustained production of a wide range of cultivated crops
$163,560 \text{ km}^2$

Class 3: Land capable of sustained production of a range of cultivated crops
$254,420 \text{ km}^2$

Class 4: Generally marginal for cultivation
$253,710 \text{ km}^2$

Class 5: Best used for pasture
$338,210 \text{ km}^2$

Class 6: Used for natural rangeland
183,630 km^2

Class 7: No capability for agricultural production
612,650 km^2

Total land area: 9,221,300 km^2

Source: Environment Canada, *Canada's Special Resource Lands*

Agriculture by Province

British Columbia: Only 4% of the land is capable of agricultural production. The Okanagan Valley contains 25% of Canada's best fruitland and produces 43% of its tree-fruit crop.

Alberta, Saskatchewan and Manitoba: Almost 80% of Canada's prime agricultural land (Classes 1, 2 and 3) is found in the three prairie provinces, which produce 55% of Canada's agricultural output and almost $10 billion in farm cash receipts annually.

Ontario: 51% of Canada's Class 1 agricultural land is in southern Ontario.

Quebec: 72% of Quebec's 2.2 million hectares of prime agricultural lands are found within a 160-km radius of Montreal.

New Brunswick: 47% of the province's land has agricultural capabilities of Classes 2-4.

Nova Scotia: Nova Scotia contains 2.5%, or 1.15 million hectares, of Canada's prime agricultural capability land.

Prince Edward Island: 71.5% of the island is prime agricultural land, the highest percentage contained in any one province.

Urbanization of Rural Land: From Foodland to Wasteland

Prime agricultural land in Canada is increasingly being converted to urban uses. Over 55% of the best agricultural land in Canada (Classes 1-3) lies within a 160-km radius of large urban centres. When cities spread, they do so at the expense of prime agricultural land.

Between 1976 and 1981 approximately 98,976 hectares of rural land were converted to urban uses. Fifty percent of this land had high capability for agricultural production. Once converted, the land is virtually lost as far as food production goes.

Agricultural Soil Capability in Canada

The shaded areas show soils capable of maintaining field crops (Canada Land Inventory Classes 1-4).

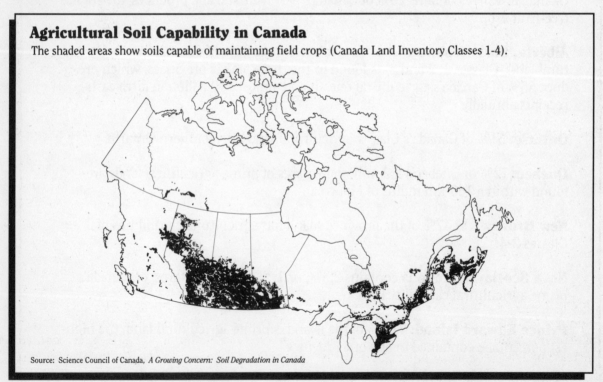

Source: Science Council of Canada, *A Growing Concern: Soil Degradation in Canada*

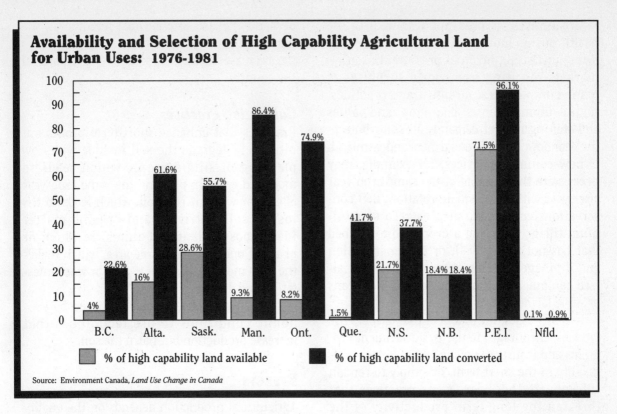

Availability and Selection of High Capability Agricultural Land for Urban Uses: 1976-1981

	% of high capability land available	% of high capability land converted
B.C.	4%	22.6%
Alta.	16%	61.6%
Sask.	28.6%	55.7%
Man.	9.3%	86.4%
Ont.	8.2%	74.9%
Que.	1.5%	41.7%
N.S.	21.7%	37.7%
N.B.	18.4%	18.4%
P.E.I.	71.5%	96.1%
Nfld.	0.1%	0.9%

Source: Environment Canada, *Land Use Change in Canada*

Quebec and Ontario experience the most acute competition for farmland, as 38% of all Class 1 lands in Canada lie in the areas around Montreal and Toronto. In Ontario, 4% of the total Class 1 agricultural land in the province was converted to urban uses between 1976 and 1981, at an average rate of 46 hectares for every increase of 1,000 in urban population. In Quebec, 45% of the land urbanized around Montreal between 1976 and 1981 was of prime agricultural capability, with 191 hectares lost per increase of 1,000 in population. Ironically, it is the high quality of the soil around these cities that made settlement desirable in the first place, yet the cities are now taking over that productive land.

CAUSES

Agriculture is one of Canada's largest industries, providing jobs directly for over half a million people, and accounting for approximately 10% of the gross domestic product, with annual sales of over $50 billion. In 1984, Canada exported over $9.8 billion worth of agricultural products.

Urbanization is not the only threat to the health of this industry. Canadian farmers are facing increasing financial pressure. Uncertain markets resulting from world surpluses of many commodities, foreign trade practices, high equipment costs, changing land values and shifting market demands all contribute to the economic stresses on farmers and farmland.

Low commodity prices, for example, may necessitate the planting of the same crop year after year without adequate rotation. Soil conservation techniques, such as zero or minimum tillage (planting a crop into a seedbed that has not been tilled), or proper irrigation and drainage systems, often require specialized equipment that may be beyond the means of some farmers.

In many cases, the practices that farmers use (and are encouraged to use by government programs and insurance policies) to maintain profitability in the short term, or simply to remain solvent, are those very same practices that threaten the long-term productivity of the farm. Crop insurance regulations, for example, may require that farmers plant on bare soil, even though stubble cropping (or planting new seed directly into soil that retains last year's unploughed stubble) reduces soil erosion and enhances soil productivity. Methods used to increase production often take their toll on the soil.

Chemical Fertilizers

In order to increase yields on increasingly degraded soil, current agricultural practices demand the use of chemical fertilizers. The increased use of nitrogen fertilizer has led to the increased acidity of soils in many parts of the country.

Cultivation Practices

Practices that enhance short-term profits but ultimately degrade the soil include wide-row planting of single crops, which leads to increased erosion; planting the same crop year after year without rotation, which leads to the loss of soil nutrients and organic matter (decomposed plant and animal residue); or planting one crop in a large area, which makes the crop more susceptible to pest or weed infestation and disease.

In each case, the farmer is forced by economic conditions to use techniques that increase production but harm the soil.

EFFECTS

Agricultural production depends on the quality of soil, particularly its nutrient and organic matter content. If the soil is not under cultivation, the natural decaying process returns nutrients and organic matter to the soil. The decayed material, called humus, not only adds nutrients, but also helps the soil retain moisture and helps to stop erosion.

When crops are grown, cultivated and harvested, the nutrient content of the soil is reduced (taken up by the plants) and, depending on the tilling and harvesting techniques, organic matter may be reduced.

Compaction: Process that results in less pore space in the soil; caused by impact, such as heavy machinery on wet soil.

Erosion: Process by which soil is worn away.

Monoculture: Practice of growing the same crop on the same field year after year.

Summerfallow: Practice of leaving the land unsown (although it is ploughed and cultivated) for a season in an effort to conserve moisture and build nitrogen in the soil. Unfortunately, summerfallowing has the opposite effect: instead of conserving moisture, summerfallowing leads to increased erosion and loss of organic matter.

"Soil at Risk"

Soil degradation is an ongoing, insidious problem that occurs in all parts of the country at a cost of over $3 million per day or $1.3 billion annually.
— Science Council of Canada, *A Growing Concern: Soil Degradation in Canada*

Soil degradation can take a number of different forms: loss of soil through erosion by wind and water; contamination of soil through salinization (or excessive salt), acidification and heavy metals; compaction of soil; and loss of organic matter.

All regions of Canada are affected.

Erosion

Topsoil — the upper layer of nutrient-rich material — is a renewable resource, but it takes from 300 to 1,000 years for just 2.5 cm of topsoil to develop.

Canada's farmlands were once covered by 25 to 45 cm of topsoil. Now, there is an average of only 15 cm. This makes soil erosion the most widespread threat to agricultural productivity in Canada.

"Worldwide, an estimated 25 billion tons of topsoil is being lost from cropland each year, roughly the amount that covers Australia's wheat lands."

— Lester R. Brown, et al., *State of the World 1989*

Erosion reduces the organic matter content of soil, thereby weakening soil structure, reducing its water-retaining capability and lowering productivity.

In Western Canada, erosion has severely affected almost 6 million hectares of growing land. For every bushel of grain produced on the Prairies, an estimated three bushels of soil are lost. In Quebec, up to 400,000 m^3 of topsoil are lost every year because of wind erosion.

Water erosion, which can greatly reduce agricultural productivity, occurs when the soil cannot absorb moisture from rainfall. This occurs, for example, when fields are left bare over the winter (instead of being left covered with the stubble from the last year's harvest), or when certain row crops, such as potatoes, are planted year after year without rotation.

Water Erosion

"Each year 40 hectares of Prince Edward Island get washed away into the Gulf of St. Lawrence.... At the current rate of sea erosion, PEI will disappear in 13,000 years."
— Michael Valpy in *Globe and Mail*, 1989

British Columbia: In the Peace River District, 11.5 tonnes of topsoil per hectare are lost annually on grain producing fields. Up to 25% of the land may have lost *all* topsoil as a result of erosion.

Prairies: Water erosion accounts for over half of all topsoil losses.

Ontario: From 2 to 18 tonnes of topsoil per hectare are lost in southern Ontario every year.

Quebec: In the Appalachian region, up to 50 tonnes of soil per hectare have been lost over a 4-year period.

New Brunswick: Annual losses of 20 tonnes of topsoil per hectare have been recorded.

Prince Edward Island: Losses of 20 tonnes per hectare every year have been recorded.

Nova Scotia: Up to 40 tonnes of soil per hectare have been lost annually.

Source: Science Council of Canada, *A Growing Concern: Soil Degradation in Canada*

Major Influences on Canadian Farmland

Factors

Loss of Soil Quality
- Loss of Organic Matter
- Nutrient Content
- Acidification
- Salinization
- Erosion (Wind and water)
- Compaction

Land use change
- Agriculture to Urban
- Wetlands to Agriculture

Agricultural Practices
- Monoculture (Seed Selection)
- Fertilizer Use
- Pesticide Use

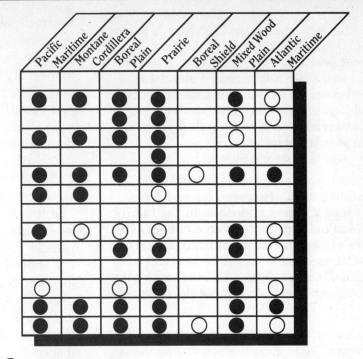

● Primary Importance   ○ Secondary Importance

Source: Environment Canada, *State of the Environment Report for Canada, 1986*

Costs of Soil Degradation in Canada ($ millions)

	B.C.	Alta.	Sask.	Man.	Ont.	Que.	Atlantic	Total
Erosion	10	200	220	10	68	10	11	529
Organic Matter Loss	11	144	170	—	—	—	—	325
Acidification	5	5	50	—	1	4	6	71
Salinity	—	80	120	12	—	—	—	212
Compaction	12	—	—	—	21	100	6	139

Source: D. A. Rennie, *Soil and Water Issues and Options in Canada*, quoted in Science Council of Canada, *A Growing Concern*

Pesticides

Getting into the pesticide debate is asking to be insulted. If you voice concerns about pesticides you are likely to be told that you are a misinformed idealist who has become a victim of irrational fears: and if you speak for pesticides you might be referred to as a profiteering polluter and people poisoner.
— Stuart B. Hill, in *Agrologist*, Winter 1983

Agriculture Canada does not promote pesticide use.... However, it's one thing to spend a sunny afternoon in the family garden pulling weeds from a couple of rows of carrots; it's an entirely different matter to hand-weed 1,000 hectares of Manitoba wheatfields. A farmer who hired enough people to do this would go broke.
— Agriculture Canada, *Pesticides in Perspective*

Agricultural areas treated with pesticides increased by an average 300% during the 70s, and up to 500% in some locations. In 1986 Canadian farmers spent $694 million on pesticides.

There is nothing biologically specific to any plant or insect that makes it a pest; rather, we label certain weeds or bugs pests because they interfere with the production of crops that we have deemed beneficial.

From this perspective, pests are not the *causes* of problems, but rather the symptoms of a poorly designed or mismanaged system, in which certain elements are upsetting the balance. The causes of the imbalance may, in many cases, be found in the way the system is set up in the first place: for example, continuous cropping of a single variety over a large field makes pest infestations virtually impossible to control except through chemical input; genetic hybrids designed for maximum output may be more susceptible to pests; and crops planted in degraded soil are generally less able to withstand pest infestations.

If it is for economic reasons — to produce food in as efficient a manner as possible — that pesticides are applied, then true cost accounting should include the long-term costs of increased pesticide use.

For example, along with killing economically undesirable weeds and insects, many pesticides also attack beneficial insects, the same ones that eradicate pests. Thus, even more pesticides have to be applied.

In addition, pests may become resistant to the effects of pesticides, developing detoxification mechanisms that render certain chemicals harmless. According to the Worldwatch Institute, in 1938 there were just 7 known insect and mite species that were resistant to pesticides; in 1984 there were 447 resistant species, including many major agricultural pests.

Beneficial Insects

Even from a human and economic point of view, the number of beneficial insects by far outweighs the number of pests.

• Fruits, vegetables and ornamentals depend on insects to pollinate their flowers.

• Insects aerate the soil by digging and burrowing, and their dead bodies and droppings provide important soil nutrients.

• Insects recycle nutrients by feeding on dead plants and animals.

• Many birds, mammals and fish depend on insects for their diet.

• Many insects feed on pests: for example, ladybird beetles control aphid populations.

Pesticides remain active in the environment after they are applied. Although the misapplication of pesticides may account for some of this accumulation, even the "safe" and "proper" handling of chemicals may result in environmental contamination. Contamination by DDT is the most famous example, and the problem by no means ended with the restriction of this particular chemical in Canada.

"Q. How safe are pesticides?
A. No one can provide iron-clad assurances that each and every pesticide is completely safe all the time. Many of them are poisons.

"Q. So pesticide use involves a calculated risk?
A. Yes, there is risk. It would be foolish and dishonest for anyone to suggest that there isn't...all pesticides are made to kill living organisms. If they weren't, they wouldn't do their job."

— Agriculture Canada, "Let's Talk About Pesticides"

Pesticide residues enter the environment in a number of different ways. When pesticides are aerially applied on crops, they can drift in the wind. When chemicals are applied directly on crops, some residues may filter through soil to the groundwater, or water run-off from fields may contaminate rivers and streams. The disposal of pesticide containers and spray equipment may also lead to environmental contamination.

Although controversy surrounds the issue of pesticide use, there is agreement on one fact: pesticides are poisons. Uncertainty and debate arise when one tries to evaluate just what effects these chemicals will have on the environment, at what levels of exposure, over how long and in combination with what other chemicals.

"Most information available on farm work and cancer finds that farmers generally have a rate of death from *all types of cancer* combined that is lower than the death rate from cancer for the rest of the population.... However, there are *higher* than average risks for *some groups of farmers* for *particular types of cancer*, such as leukemia, stomach cancer, lip cancer, prostate cancer, and aplastic anemia."

— Canadian Centre for Occupational Health and Safety, *Farming and Cancer*

Spraying Brushkill in New Brunswick

" 'It was a great summer job. Everyone loved it,' said Jerry White, a stocky 48-year-old former salesman.

"White worked the summers of 1956 and 1957. He, some other high school boys and some older men were hired to clear brush from the power-line paths through the woods by spraying weed killer [Brushkill] on the undergrowth....

"At the time, none of the young sprayers gave it a second thought.

" 'As far as we were concerned, we were just spraying water,' White said. 'It would get hot and we'd get in fights with it, one crew against another. We'd spray each other, like water fights.'..."

"Glenn Glicks, 54, remembered 'swimming in it.' He said that he would get right down into a large tank of the solution (usually mixed one to five gallons of Brushkill to 100 gallons of water) while cleaning leaves out of the filter.

" 'It didn't taste all that bad,' he grinned. . . .

" 'Everyone had been told that it was safe enough to drink,' said White.

"Wayne Hunter, 50, remembered how one man — either from Dow or the power commission — demonstrated that Brushkill was safe.

" 'He just dipped his hand into the solution and took a mouthful,' Hunter said."

— *Detroit Free Press*, January 13, 1987

Of the 204 original Brushkill sprayers who have been traced, 79 have died. Their mortality rate is more than 200% higher than that of the general New Brunswick population.

The "great summer job" has resulted in a lawsuit against Dow Chemical and the New Brunswick Power Commission by the Sprayers of Dioxin Association (SODA), based in New Brunswick.

The Canadian Environmental Defence Fund is representing SODA.

SOLUTIONS

The cost to the general public of arresting, or at least mitigating, the decline of agricultural soils in Canada will be high. However, the long-term cost of continuing to engage in exploitive agriculture, or of failing to alter the economic circumstances that encourage soil degradation, will definitely be higher.
— Science Council of Canada, *A Growing Concern: Soil Degradation in Canada*

It is clear that farmers do not set out to contaminate the environment or to degrade the soil they depend on. Instead, they are working within and responding to existing economic and production systems that often promote short-term increases in productivity at the expense of long-term viability. Nevertheless, there are alternatives that farmers will be forced to consider.

Sustainable Agriculture
The American Society of Agronomy defines sustainable agriculture as a practice that "enhances environmental quality and agriculture's resource base; provides basic human food

and fiber requirements; is economically viable; enhances the quality of life for farmers and society as a whole" (*cognition*, April 1989). Across Canada, there are many proponents of agricultural practices that do not "cost the earth," practices that can be sustained in the long term. Alternative agricultural models are known under a variety of labels — ecological, regenerative, sustainable, permanent, organic, biodynamic, biological or, simply, natural agriculture. Although they differ in a number of significant ways, these models are united by one principle: agricultural production should be recognized as an integrated system, a unified whole in which the imbalances in one part (e.g., continuous cropping) have a negative effect in another (e.g. increased pest infestation), and in which the farmer is the "steward" of the land, taking care of it, regenerating rather than exhausting it for future generations.

The alternatives offered by such models include biological methods of pest control rather than use of synthetic chemicals, recycling organic matter to replenish the soil, low impact cultivation techniques, planting trees and shrubs to act as windbreaks to impede erosion, and encouraging genetic diversity of crops to reduce pest infestations.

"*Country Guide*, the flagship publication of Winnipeg-based Public Press, a division of United Grain Growers Limited, asked its readers in an informal survey if they thought their farm's productivity would be drastically reduced 'if all crop-protection chemicals were suddenly withdrawn from the market.' Of the respondents, 52 percent said 'yes' and 48 percent said 'no.'"

— Michael Webster in *Harrowsmith*

"It is indeed possible to farm successfully without the use of insecticides, herbicides and artificial fertilizers. Economically, the farmers considered themselves to be as viable as conventional farmers.... The farmers also have fewer problems with insects, weeds, plant diseases and erosion than conventional farmers, as their agricultural practices are preventative as well as curative."

— Canadian Organic Growers, *Problems Facing Canadian Farmers Using Organic Agricultural Methods*

Genetic Diversity in Agricultural Production

Canada cannot afford to be complacent with regard to its animal genetic resources.... There is an urgent need for Canadians to undertake conservation action as both short-term and long-term insurance against changing needs.

— R. Crawford, University of Saskatchewan

Genetic diversity (i.e., the different species on earth and the variations within species) is the basis on which new strains of plants and animals are developed. However, the demands of intensive agriculture mean that value is placed on relatively few genetic traits: maximum efficiency through such features as uniform ripening, hardiness and maximum size is usually the basis of evaluation.

The result is that diversity of the agricultural gene pool may be declining. For example, 75% of Canada's wheat crop is based on just four varieties of wheat, making the whole system more vulnerable to crop infestation and disease.

Although not equally restricted, livestock production is also geared towards genetic uniformity, with a small number of breeds meeting specialized production needs. However, many "minor" livestock breeds, which may not be the most efficient producers by today's standards, do represent an invaluable gene pool. If these rare breeds are allowed to die off, we may lose genetic resources for future breeding.

The Joywind Farm Rare Breeds Conservancy is at the forefront of Canadian efforts to preserve rare livestock breeds. Gail Chiperzak, co-founder with Jy Chiperzak of the conservancy, outlines their main aim: "We wanted to do something positive — some environmentally or ecologically sound action that actually made a difference."

The conservancy has a network of members across Canada. They monitor the livestock sector and in emergencies will try to find buyers for rare breeds on the auction block, potentially to be lost forever. If necessary, the Chiperzaks will buy the animals themselves and raise them on their farm. And with a growing semen bank, they also maintain a genetic pool that is available to farmers wishing to conserve rare breeds.

The direct action of these two individuals is helping to ensure the viability of future livestock production and to publicize the need for rare breed conservancy.

Joywind Farm Rare Breeds Conservancy Inc. is a registered charitable membership organization that issues tax receipts for donations. They publish a quarterly newsletter and sell T-shirts and sweat shirts with the Joywind Farm logo. The address is R.R. #4, Marmora, Ontario K0K 2M0; (613) 395-3268.

What Can I Do?

- If you have any questions about sustainable agriculture, contact the Ecological Agriculture Project at Macdonald College in Quebec (see source list for address). The project operates the Farm Info Network and will provide information on a wide range of topics. Write for a list of publications, many of which are under $1.

- If you are an agricultural worker, the most important environmental action you can take is to become a steward of the soil, ensuring its health for future generations. Don't poison it with toxic chemicals; do rotate crops, plant cover crops in the fall, establish windbreaks, preserve wetlands and other "marginal" areas, stabilize stream edges with vegetation, and recycle plant and animal nutrients back into the soil. Contact any of the provincial sustainable agriculture or organic crop improvement associations for more information.

- An organization called Willing Workers on Organic Farms matches young people interested in working on organic farms with farmers throughout Canada. For information, contact John Vanden Heuvel at R.R. #2, Nelson, British Columbia V1L 5P5; (604) 354-4417.

- Your provincial ministry of agriculture may have programs to support farmers adopting conservation practices. The Ontario Land Stewardship Program, for example, provides grants to farmers to plant trees to prevent erosion. Contact your provincial agriculture ministry. (See source list for addresses.)

- The three prairie provinces have started recycling programs for farm chemical containers, in an effort to keep pesticides from contaminating groundwater and soil. For details about the program, contact your provincial environment ministry.

- There are many sources of information on sustainable agriculture in Canada. Start with government, if only to emphasize the fact that there are members of the public who want this type of information. Both Agriculture Canada and the provincial agriculture ministries should be able to refer you to appropriate groups or sources of information. Although the governments are not yet producing a great deal of material on organic agriculture, they are a source of information on certain *aspects* of sustainable agriculture (for example, pest identification, saving energy on the farm and planting windbreaks), most of which is provided free of charge.

  There are also farm organizations across Canada that will provide information on sustainable agriculture (see source list). The provincial environment network can also direct you to these groups.

- Canadian Organic Growers has an extensive library of books, articles and resources on organic production. These are available to members. (See source list.)

- Even those who are not involved directly in agricultural production can make a difference.

According to the Ontario Crop Improvement Association, "A serious move away from chemical farming has to begin with consumers. Consumers must begin to think about what's in their food rather than how it looks. When more people start asking for organically grown food, more will be produced."

Organic foods (those grown without chemical pesticides or herbicides) can be found at many health food stores, food co-ops, directly at local farms, and even in some major grocery chains. By choosing organically-grown food, not only are you ensuring that you'll be getting foods with minimum chemical residues, but you will also be supporting those farmers who are committed to stewardship of the soil and land. The more people who ask for organic food, the more pressure there will be on retailers to supply it and restaurants to serve it.

• Another way to encourage a sustainable agriculture system is to support local growers. Transportation of food takes energy and by buying produce from local farmers, the amount of energy expended in transportation is kept to a minimum. (As well, food imported from other countries may have been grown using pesticides that are banned from use in Canada.) It may be difficult to find local produce at major grocery chains; you may have to ask around at smaller greengrocers or at food co-ops (which, in general, do try to buy from local producers). Alternatively, buy from farmers' markets, roadside stands or directly from the farm.

Canadian Organic Growers has produced and published a directory of organic farmers who sell pesticide-free produce directly from their farms. A list of British Columbia's organic farmers is available from the B.C. Organic Growers, Box 11, Lytton, British Columbia V0K 1Z0. Many of the provincial sustainable or organic agriculture groups will provide a list of organic growers on request.

• North American consumption of beef is contributing to a number of environmental problems: destruction of tropical rainforests, the greenhouse effect (cows belch methane, one of the greenhouse gases) and the inequities in the global food system. Limit your consumption of beef.

• If you are concerned about the urbanization of agricultural lands in your area, contact your provincial environment network to find out what groups are working on this issue. They'll need help!

• There are many groups across the country working on issues related to pesticide use and abuse. It is through their efforts that the pesticide issue is kept in the public eye. You may wish to contact groups in your area for more information, or to offer help. (See source list for addresses.)

Wilderness:
No Place to Go

I feel like a policeman that's trying to catch this
criminal called the Crown. If I were a judge, I
would sentence this Crown to life: life on the land,
in the hope that over time this Crown would realize
that Nature is the boss.

— CHIEF GARY POTTS, TEME-AUGAMA ANISHNABAI, *TEMAGAMI WILDERNESS*, SUMMER 1988

THE PROBLEM:

We're bulldozing our way through wilderness, overcutting forests,
flooding ecosystems, contaminating and eliminating wildlife habitat.

THE SOLUTION:

Consider the impact that our development has already had on the
environment; ensure that our activities do not destroy the ability of
species and ecosystems to renew themselves.

Definition

"Nature" seems to be taking on quotation marks: something ersatz, manufactured or simulated — the label on a cereal box. Wilderness is becoming something to be protected, conserved, even "managed" or enhanced, not something that simply *is*.

We live on the land, but do we live with the land? To what extent do our practices endanger the other forms of life with which we share the planet? Do we consider the basic features of our "home" (the soil, water, plants, minerals, etc.) as resources just waiting to be exploited? Is economics the bottom line, the measure of all growth?

These are just some of the questions that we have to ask ourselves as increased economic pressures place environmental concerns in conflict with the demands of development. The real bottom line, the bottom line on which every economic model depends, on which every living thing depends, is a healthy environment.

Causes

We abuse the land because we regard it as a commodity belonging to us. When we see land as a community to which we belong, we may begin to use it with love and respect.
— Aldo Leopold

Our political, economic and social structures demand growth. But what fuels this progress and how is it measured? In a resource-based economy such as ours, growth often depends on developing the resources of land and water, and the measure of success is usually defined in terms of the commodities produced and sold.

However, resources *are* finite, and the extent of wilderness is limited. It may seem alarmist in a country the size of Canada to talk of limited wilderness, but if we take the example of wetlands (just one threatened ecosystem), then the problem is amply illustrated.

Wetlands, which cover 14% of Canada or 1.27 million km^2 of land, are areas that are seasonally or permanently covered with shallow water. They include swamps, marshes, bogs, ponds and saltwater flats.

Wetlands soak up rain and melting snow during periods of high runoff and slowly release the water during drier times. Wetlands have been called "nature's kidneys" because of their function as filters, allowing sediment to settle out and reducing pollution.

Wetlands are also of prime importance as habitat for many animals, providing breeding, nesting and mating grounds for ducks, fish, many birds and other animals.

However, wetlands such as marshes and swamps are often considered to be wasted spaces, areas to be drained and converted to more "productive" uses. This attitude has resulted in the loss of over half the original wetlands in southern Canada. Wetlands that have been lost to development and conversion include 65% of Atlantic coastal marshes, 90% of wetlands in southwestern Ontario, 70% in

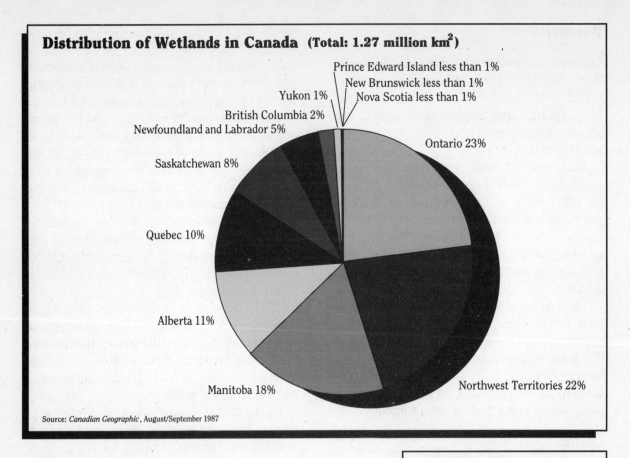

Distribution of Wetlands in Canada (Total: 1.27 million km²)

Prince Edward Island less than 1%
New Brunswick less than 1%
Nova Scotia less than 1%
Yukon 1%
British Columbia 2%
Newfoundland and Labrador 5%
Saskatchewan 8%
Quebec 10%
Alberta 11%
Manitoba 18%
Ontario 23%
Northwest Territories 22%

Source: *Canadian Geographic*, August/September 1987

southern Quebec, 71% of Prairie wetlands and 80% of the Fraser River delta in British Columbia. Thus, even in this huge country, wetlands have disappeared at an alarming rate. Such wide-scale ecosystem loss has had a deleterious effect on farmland, water cycles and many forms of wildlife.

Function of Wetlands
• Wildlife habitat;
• Storing excess floodwater;
• Stabilizing streamflows;
• Purifying runoff;
• Absorbing pollutants;
• Recharging groundwater;
• Trapping silt;
• Controlling salinity of soil;
• Controlling water erosion.

EFFECTS

Without habitat, there is no wildlife. It's that simple.
— Wildlife Habitat Canada

As we drain wetlands to make way for urban development and industrial or agricultural development, as we pave over agricultural soil for urban growth, as we clearcut temperate rainforests for their lumber, not only are we destroying habitat; we are also eradicating complex ecosystems that regulate water cycles and feed the soil.

Nowhere does the clash between development issues and wilderness conservation become more acute than in threatened areas. Carmanah in British Columbia, tall-grass ecosystems in the Prairies, Temagami in Ontario, sand dunes in Prince Edward Island are just a few of the recent battlegrounds.

The development-versus-conservation fight is often drawn along lines that go something like this: "This is an area that has a valuable resource that we want to tap" (trees to feed the forestry industry; coastal properties for prime tourist development, etc.) versus "This is an area that has a valuable resource we want to protect."

In both sides of this equation, wilderness is seen as a resource, something that exists for humans (either for our exploitation or for our enjoyment). Once the inherent self-interest of this attitude has been identified, even some conservation efforts take on an unhealthy glow. Take Environment Canada's approach, for example: "Protecting places which are *signifi-cant examples* of Canada's natural and cultural heritage....The need to conserve *outstanding natural areas*...." Does this mean that wilderness is important only in terms of representative "pockets" or "examples"? Are we trying to turn the country into a museum or zoo, where only "outstanding" wilderness is on display?

Endangered Species

Paul Ehrlich likened [wildlife extinction] to rivets popping out of a jet aircraft; you could remove a few rivets and perhaps nothing will happen, but eventually one rivet too many will be removed and the whole plane falls apart and crashes.
— Monte Hummel, World Wildlife Fund

In 1977 The Committee on the Status of Endangered Wildlife in Canada (COSEWIC) was established to identify species that are threatened with extinction. This joint federal and provincial agency has no legal power to protect the plants and animals that it identifies as threatened; rather it reviews scientific literature and then designates species according to one of its five categories:

- **Rare:** An indigenous species of flora or fauna that exists in very low numbers in restricted areas and is, therefore, vulnerable but not yet a threatened species.

- **Threatened:** An indigenous species that is likely to become endangered if present trends that are adversely affecting the population continue.

Degree of Impact By Human Activities on Wildlife Habitat in Canada

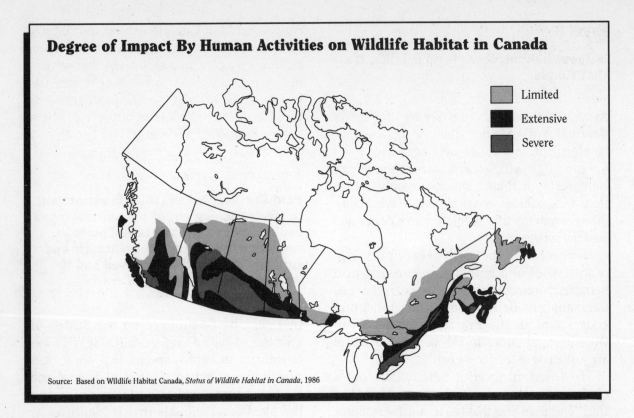

Limited
Extensive
Severe

Source: Based on Wildlife Habitat Canada, *Status of Wildlife Habitat in Canada*, 1986

- **Endangered:** An indigenous species that is threatened with immediate extinction or extirpation because of human activity.

- **Extirpated:** An indigenous species that no longer exists in the wild in Canada but does exist elsewhere.

- **Extinct:** A formerly indigenous species that no longer exists.

Although the number of plants and animals on the COSEWIC list continues to increase, there are examples of threatened animals being removed because of positive changes to their population. The White Pelican, for example, was designated as "threatened" for years, but in 1987 was "delisted" after its population grew to 50,000 pairs. The Wood Bison was the first species to be "downlisted," that is, moved from endangered to threatened.

There were 183 species on the COSEWIC list in 1989.

Major Habitat Issues and Effects

The major activities affecting wildlife habitat in Canada have been enumerated by the national agency Wildlife Habitat Canada in its 1986 report, *The Status of Wildlife Habitat in Canada.*

Atlantic Region

- Forestry: Habitat loss from inadequate reforestation; contamination due to use of herbicides.

- Agriculture: 65% of Maritime wetlands have been diked for agricultural purposes; siltation of fish habitat as a result of agricultural practices.

- Resource Development: Hydroelectric and mineral exploration.

- Tourism: Development and increased accessibility of sand dunes, beaches, wetlands, etc.

- Pollution: Acid rain.

Quebec

- Urban Development: Loss of wetlands (over 3,600 hectares); sewage dumping in waterways.

- Pollution: Acid rain; toxic contamination.

- Military: Low-level military jet training flights disrupting wildlife.

- Resource Development: Hydroelectric projects.

Ontario

- Urban Development: Loss of wetlands (80% of the original 2 to 2.4 million hectares lost or severely altered).

- Agriculture: Draining of wetlands; pesticide and herbicide contamination of water.

- Forestry: Modification and loss of habitat.

- Pollution: Acid rain; toxic contamination of water, soil and air.

Prairies

- Agriculture: Drainage of wetlands (40% of original total lost); conversion of native grasslands (less than 1% of original grasslands remain).

- Tourism: Disruption of sensitive areas.

- Development: Flooding through hydroelectric projects and expanding gas, oil and coal development.

British Columbia

- Forestry: Current forestry practices; ineffective reforestation; destabilization of river banks.

- Agriculture: Conversion of wetlands.

- Development: Hydro and mining projects.

Yukon and Northwest Territories

- Resource Development: Mining; oil and gas exploration and production.

- Pollution: Toxic contamination.

COSEWIC's 1989 List of Endangered Species in Canada

	Mammals		Birds		Reptiles and Amphibians
Extinct	Dawson Caribou Sea Mink		Great Auk Labrador Duck Passenger Pigeon		
Extirpated	Atlantic Grey Whale Atlantic Walrus (St. Lawrence Population) Black-footed Ferret Swift Fox				
Endangered	Bowhead Whale Eastern Cougar Eastern Wolverine Right Whale St. Lawrence River Beluga Whale Sea Otter Ungava Bay Beluga Whale Vancouver Island Marmot		Eskimo Curlew Greater Prairie Chicken Kirtland's Warbler Mountain Plover Peregrine Falcon (subspecies anatum) Piping Plover Spotted Owl Whooping Crane		Leatherback Turtle
Threatened	Eastmain Beluga Whale Maritime Woodland Caribou Newfoundland Pine Marten North Pacific Humpback Whale Peary Caribou Prairie Long-tailed Weasel Wood Bison		Baird's Sparrow Burrowing Owl Ferruginous Hawk Henslow's Sparrow Loggerhead Shrike Peregrine Falcon (subspecies tundrius) Roseate Tern		
Vulnerable	Sowerby's Beaked Whale Western Wolverine				Northern Prairie Skink Pacific Giant Salamander

Rare	Black-tailed
	  Prairie Dog
	Blue Whale
	Eastern Mole
	Fin Whale
	Fringed Myotis
	Gaspé Shrew
	Grey Fox
	Keen's Long-eared Bat
	Northwest Atlantic Humpback Whale
		Pallid Bat
		Plains Pocket Gopher
		Queen Charlotte Islands Ermine
		Spotted Bat
		Southern Flying Squirrel
		Western Woodland Caribou
			Barn Owl
			Caspian Tern
			Cooper's Hawk
			Eastern Bluebird
			Flammulated Owl
			Great Gray Owl
			Ipswich Sparrow
			Ivory Gull
			King Rail
			Least Bittern
				Peregrine Falcon
				  (subspecies pealei)
				Prairie Warbler
				Prothonotary Warbler
				Red-shouldered Hawk
				Ross's Gull
				Trumpeter Swan
					Fowler's Toad

Delisted			White Pelican		
Downlisted	Wood Bison				

Source: World Wildlife Fund

COSEWIC's 1989 List of Endangered Species in Canada

	Fish		Plants		
Extinct	Banff Longnose Dace Blue Walleye	Deepwater Cisco Longjaw Cisco			
Extirpated	Gravel Chub Paddle Fish		Blue-eyed Mary		
Endangered	Acadian Whitefish Aurora Trout Salish Sucker		Cucumber Tree Eastern Mountain Avens Eastern Prickly Pear Cactus Furbish's Lousewort Gattinger's Agalinis Heart-leaved Plantain Hoary Mountain Mint Large Whorled Pogonia Pink Coreopsis	Pink Milkwort Skinner's Agalinis Slender Bush Clover Southern Maidenhair Fern Small White Lady's Slipper Small Whorled Pogonia Spotted Wintergreen Water-pennywort	
Threatened	Black Redhorse Blackfin Cisco Copper Redhorse Enos Lake Stickleback Great Lakes Deep-water Sculpin Lake Simcoe Whitefish	Margined Madtom Shorthead Sculpin Shortjaw Cisco Shortnose Cisco	American Chestnut American Waterwillow Athabasca Thrift Blue Ash Bluehearts Colicroot	Giant Helleborine Ginseng Golden Crest Kentucky Coffee Tree Mosquito Fern Nodding Pogonia	Pitcher's Thistle Plymouth Gentian Purple Twayblade Red Mulberry Sweet Pepperbush Tyrrell's Willow
Vulnerable	Banded Killifish (Newfoundland Population) Bering Wolffish Bigmouth Buffalo Black Buffalo Blackline Prickleback	Fourhorn Sculpin Least Darter Orangespotted Sunfish Redbreasted Sunfish River Darter	Gulf of St. Lawrence Aster		
Rare	Bigmouth Buffalo Bigmouth Shiner Blackstripe Topminnow Brindled Madtom Central Stoneroller Charlotte Unarmoured Stickleback Giant Stickleback Green Sturgeon Kiyi Lake Lamprey Pacific Sardine Pugnose Minnow	Pugnose Shiner Redside Dace River Redhorse Shortnose Sturgeon Silver Chub Silver Shiner Speckled Dace Spotted Gar Spotted Sucker Squanga Whitefish Umatilla Dace	Broad Beech-fern Dense Blazing Star Dwarf Hackberry Few-flowered Club-rush Green Dragon Hill's Pondweed Hop tree Indian Plantain Lilaeopsis	Macoun's Meadow-foam Prairie Rose Prairie White-fringed Orchid Shumard Oak Soapweed Swamp Rose Mallow Victorin's Gentian Victorin's Water Hemlock Western Silver-leafed Aster	
Delisted					
Downlisted					

Source: World Wildlife Fund

> "There are 198 mammal species, 550 bird species, 86 species of amphibians and reptiles, 177 freshwater fish species, about 1000 species of molluscs and well over 100,000 known species of insects and other invertebrates in Canada."
>
> — Environment Canada, *Environmental Issues in Canada: A Status Report*, 1985

Canada's Vanishing Forests

Each year, forestry companies cut the equivalent of a swath a mile wide across Canada, and replant only a fraction of that.
— Rosemary Speirs, *Toronto Star*, March 13, 1989

Let's cut down the trees and create jobs.
— British Columbia Premier William Vander Zalm, quoted in *Quotations From Chairman Zalm*, 1988

Media coverage of the battle to "save" Canada's forests often focusses on disputes between major logging companies fighting to retain industry and a handful of environmentalists trying to save "big trees." This is a misleading and highly emotional representation of a complex issue.

Like any other ecosystem, forests are intricate and diverse biological webs, comprising many different species and organisms from microbes in the soil, to mosses, lichen, amphibians, insects, birds, shrubs, ferns, etc. Alter one part of the system and there will be changes. The question, of course, is: does the change drastically alter and even damage the whole system? This is where the question of forestry *practices* becomes the key.

Clearcutting: The practice of cutting down everything that is standing in the forest in order to extract timber. Unwanted timber is left to rot, as is everything in the forest that "gets in the way." Although this practice is considered economically efficient, it can lead to landslides, erosion, degradation of the soil, complete loss of habitat for wildlife and plant species, and the impossibility of using the area for any other activity. In British Columbia, approximately 89% of all logging is done by clearcutting.

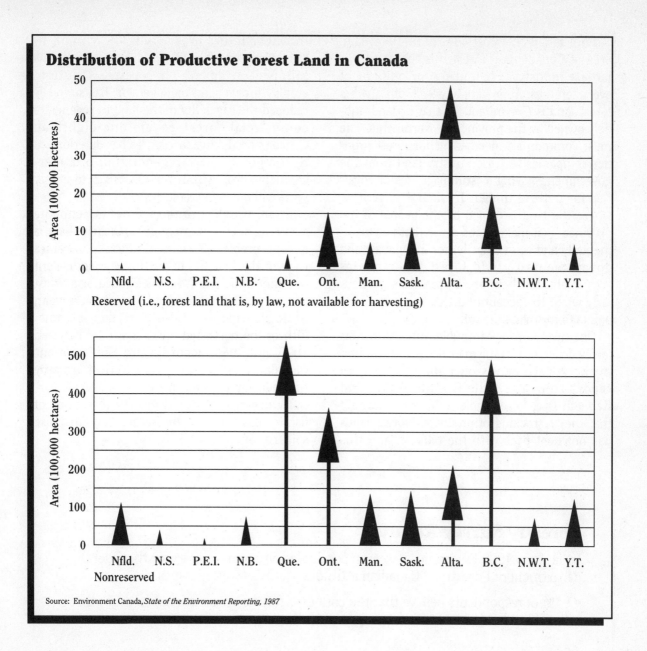

Distribution of Productive Forest Land in Canada

Area (100,000 hectares)

Nfld. N.S. P.E.I. N.B. Que. Ont. Man. Sask. Alta. B.C. N.W.T. Y.T.

Reserved (i.e., forest land that is, by law, not available for harvesting)

Area (100,000 hectares)

Nfld. N.S. P.E.I. N.B. Que. Ont. Man. Sask. Alta. B.C. N.W.T. Y.T.

Nonreserved

Source: Environment Canada, *State of the Environment Reporting, 1987*

Forests cover almost 45% of the total land area of Canada, and forestry is the country's largest industry, accounting for one out of every ten jobs. Approximately 92% of Canada's forest land is Crown land — that is, land publicly owned by the provincial governments. The most common arrangement is for forest product companies to lease forestry land from the government, paying a "stumpage" fee or royalties for cutting timber. In such a system — where the land is owned by the people of the province — it makes good sense (both environmentally and economically) for individuals and governments to hold forestry companies accountable for their forestry practices, particularly when the accounting that has been done points to mismanagement.

One need not look to public interest groups for evidence of this mismanagement: it's found in the government's own analysis. A 1989 report from the federal Auditor-General Kenneth Dye, for example, contains a warning that the "restocking of productive forest lands has not kept pace with the harvest, and this threatens future productivity." Environment Canada, in its 1985 *Status Report*, also points to mismanagement: "In forestry, failure to employ proper land management has seriously reduced the capability of the land to regenerate commercial forest cover; one-eighth of Canada's productive forest area has deteriorated to the point where regeneration of a merchantable crop within the next sixty to eighty years will not be possible."

Such official pronouncements echo the concerns of environmentalists. Clearly there is a major problem if we permit forest companies to reap the benefits of cutting the equivalent of a mile-wide swath across Canada or a forest the size of Prince Edward Island every year, while allowing them also to replant just one-fifth of the harvested area (as we did between 1975 and 1980, according to Environment Canada); or if the forestry practices used by the industry threaten habitats (of species partially dependent on old-growth forests or of fish in coastal rivers, for example) and increase soil erosion.

Forestry Survey Results

In January 1989 Environics Research conducted a national survey for the federal department of Forestry of Canadian attitudes towards forestry issues.

• 94% of respondents believe that the country's forests are a national treasure that should be held in trust for future generations.

- 27% believe that the most important use of forest lands in Canada is wildlife protection; 25% answered wilderness preservation; 12% believe that logging is the most important use of forest lands.

- 84% believe that the forestry industry has damaged the environmental quality of Canada's forests.

- Seven out of ten oppose the use of pesticides and herbicides in Canada's forests.

- Nine out of ten believe that pesticides and herbicides pose a hazard to fish and wildlife; seven out of ten believe that they pose health hazards to people near sprayed areas.

- One in two believes that too many trees are being logged.

- 65% believe that trees are not being replanted fast enough.

British Columbia's Temperate Rainforests

The term *rainforest* conjures up lush images of the Amazon, where such forests are under threat of logging and development. But Canada has some of the world's finest temperate rainforests and they, too, are under increasing threat.

The trees in the coastal temperate rainforests in British Columbia are hundreds of years old; some are over 1,000. The tallest known tree — the Carmanah Giant in the Carmanah Valley, virtually the last unlogged valley in the southern half of Vancouver Island — stands 95 metres high, taller than the Peace Tower at the Parliament Buildings in Ottawa and almost as tall as the MacMillan Bloedel Building in Vancouver.

On the British Columbia coast, approximately 185,600 hectares of old-growth forest are protected from logging. Environmentalists are fighting to save old-growth forests from logging interests, arguing that once these forests are clearcut, they will take hundreds (perhaps thousands) of years to grow again — if indeed they *are* able to grow again on degraded and eroded soil. At the current rate of cutting (over 260,000 hectares in 1987), *all* of British Columbia's remaining old-growth coastal forests that are accessible to forest companies could be cut in just under two decades.

> "In 1988 MacMillan Bloedel declared net [earnings] of $330 million. Compare that to the five-year federal/provincial Forest Resource Development Agreement (FRDA) to repair forest lands not properly reforested. The cost? $300 million."
>
> — Sierra Club of Western Canada, *Canada's Vanishing Temperate Rainforest*

The solutions to the problems of forestry mismanagement are the same as those for many environmental issues: only when forestry is practised in a sustainable manner, only when trees cut are replaced with seedlings, only when selective logging guarantees the survival of a whole living ecosystem, will a public resource be managed in a way that ensures its future existence.

SOLUTIONS

Clearly, all human activity has some impact on the environment. It would be impossible to live otherwise. We are a part of a large system of interrelationships and to try to separate ourselves (on one extreme, by trying to have no impact whatsoever, or on the other, by cordoning off samples of "outstanding" ecosystems as museum display pieces) denies the basic reality of the earth as ecosystem.

However, we do have control over the degree of our impact and we can evaluate the warning signals that should direct the control we exercise. For example, about half of the birds and mammals listed by COSEWIC are found in the three prairie provinces. Clearly this sounds an alarm about extensive habitat loss. In another kind of warning signal, the Manitoba Department of Health has issued a recommendation to hunters not to eat the kidneys of moose and to limit consumption of moose liver. This raises the alarm about toxic contamination of wildlife and wildlife habitat. Such signals of negative human impact are everywhere and the extent of the damage will only spread unless something is done — by everyone.

WHAT CAN I DO?

- The largest threat to Canadian wildlife is habitat destruction. A number of groups in Canada — Wildlife Habitat Canada, The Nature Conservancy of Canada, The Nature Trust of British Columbia, Ducks Unlimited, Saskatchewan Natural History Society, Saskatchewan Wildlife Federation, The Ontario Heritage Foundation, Island Nature Trust, for example — take direct action by buying land and preserving it for wildlife. These groups provide information on how you can maintain your land for wildlife. They also accept donations and can tell you how to leave your land to a conservation group in your will.

- For information on private stewardship of your land, contact Wildlife Habitat Canada.

- If you are thinking of donating land for conservation purposes, you may wish to order a publication by the Environmental Law Centre in Alberta that covers the legal and tax implications of such transactions. (202—10110-124 Street, Edmonton, Alberta T5N 1P6.)

- Over 50 conservation organizations across Canada have prepared The Canadian Wilderness Charter, which calls for the protection of at least 12% of the lands and waters of Canada as recommended by the Brundtland Commission. (At present, only 2.6% of Canada is protected as true wilderness.) For information, contact the World Wildlife Fund.

- We can all make a difference by ensuring that our activities do not destroy wildlife habitat. When hiking in the wilderness, follow the "Take nothing but pictures, leave nothing but footprints" rule. See Chapter 16, "Yard and Garden," for details on how to landscape for indigenous species.

- The use of motor boats can cause shoreline erosion (from the boat's wake) and can damage bird-nesting habitat. Consider the recreational boating alternatives: canoes, rowboats and sailboats, all of which do not pollute the water with fuel, and stay clear of bird-nesting habitat.

- Wetlands are not wasted space! Are the ponds and marshes in your area under threat of development? Are they being used as local dumping grounds? Contact your ministry of natural resources or environment if you think that a wetland is in danger; or contact a local environment group.

- Non-profit conservation and naturalist groups are excellent sources of information on local wilderness issues, and they often provide detailed suggestions on what actions you can take in your own area to preserve wilderness and wildlife habitat. The World Wildlife Fund, for example, publishes the *Prairie Conservation Action Plan*, which includes numerous suggestions for Prairie landowners. The Federation of Ontario Naturalists publishes a booklet, *How to Build a Marsh*. The Natural Heritage League has produced a booklet, *Protecting Ontario's Natural Heritage Through Private Stewardship*. The Valhalla Society has published a map, "B.C.'s Endangered Wilderness." Local and provincial groups are often involved in raising money for research that is needed to advocate protection of wildlife habitat. You can make a donation or volunteer your time by contacting a conservation organization in your area.

- A few of the larger conservation groups in Canada — World Wildlife Fund, Canadian Wildlife Federation and Ducks Unlimited — have arrangements with MasterCard, whereby MasterCard makes a donation to the conservation group for every purchase made by a group member on the credit card. Thus, you can make credit work for wildlife by joining one of these groups and ordering the special credit card.

- Many conservation and naturalist groups provide a mail-order service for their members, offering a wide variety of books, calendars, magazines and T-shirts at special discounts. Some groups, such as the Western Canada Wilderness Committee, publish catalogues. Contact these groups directly for more information.

- Many provincial governments have programs to protect wilderness areas. The Ontario Ministry of Natural Resources, for example, funds individual projects to protect habitat through its Community Wildlife Involvement Program, and tax rebates are available to landowners committed to stewardship through the Ontario Conservation Land Tax Reduction Program. In Manitoba, the Ecologically Significant Areas Protection Program offers assistance to landowners concerned about conservation. There are many other programs across the country. Contact your provincial natural resources ministry to see if there are any programs in which you can get involved. Find out what legislation is in place in your province to protect wildlife habitat; write letters to the provincial environment ministry if such legislation is not in place; write in support of the legislation if it exists.

- The phrase "Buying Canadian" takes on special significance with the creation of Grasslands National Park in Saskatchewan. Through the Canadian Nature Federation and the Nature Conservancy of Canada, you can make a donation to the public financing of the park.

- As with any environmental issue, awareness is the key to action. Attitudes regarding what is acceptable and what is not change, but only when enough people are aware of the facts. For example, Chrysler Canada probably thought it had a great outdoors advertisement when it showed a family driving down a stream in a four-wheel-drive vehicle. But the Canadian Wildlife Federation quickly denounced the ad, pointing out that the implicit promotion of a destructive practice is no longer acceptable. We may be spending millions of dollars every year on habitat conservation, but we still have to be vigilant about destructive attitudes and practices.

- Work with others in your community to restore habitats. Is there a stream that is highly silted as a result of agricultural runoff? Is fish habitat threatened? Your provincial natural resources ministry should be able to help your group develop an action plan and there may be provincial or municipal funding available for your project.

- Animal populations in Canada are also threatened by illegal poaching. A number of provinces have programs to report poachers. For example, Saskatchewan has a toll-free "Turn in Poachers" telephone line (1-800-667-7561), as does British Columbia (1-800-663-9453). If you suspect that illegal hunting is occurring, contact your provincial natural resources ministry or the police.

• Find out what is being done in your province to ensure adequate regeneration of forests and proper management of a publicly-owned resource. Your findings may prove startling: in Ontario, for example, the provincial government spent $200 million in 1988 on forest management, yet collected only $82 million from forest companies. How many trees are cut down? How many are replanted? This kind of information is surprisingly hard to come by, considering that any sound forestry decision should be based on it. Talk with groups working on forestry issues and find out how you can help to ensure "forests for the future."

• Loss of habitat is the major issue affecting wildlife in Canada, but toxic contamination also poses a threat. The beluga whales in the St. Lawrence River, for example, are considered to be one of the most contaminated species on earth. The St. Lawrence National Institute of Ecotoxicology has embarked on a "Let's Adopt a Beluga" campaign, with donations being used to study and protect the remaining 500 whales.

• "It's too late to save a dinosaur, but you can still Adopt-A-Reptile," says the Reptile Breeding Foundation. Located in Picton, Ontario, this unique facility is a world leader in the active preservation of rare and endangered species of reptiles. For a donation, individuals can adopt (not to take home!) a Russian gecko or even a blood python. Contact the Reptile Breeding Foundation for more information. (See source list for address.)

• The Long Point Bird Observatory, the oldest bird observatory in Canada, also looks to private donations to fund some of its research. You can "adopt" a banded bird and help the observatory continue its work. Long Point is also co-ordinating the Ontario Lakes Loon Survey, which studies the effects of acid rain and human disturbance on common loons in Ontario. In the survey, volunteers make observations on lakes across Ontario every summer. Contact Long Point Bird Observatory for information on how to get involved.

• Circuses, marine parks and other "entertainment" that use animals for show may not be providing adequate space and exercise for the animals. Contact your local humane society for more information before supporting this use.

• When travelling, avoid buying products made from animal skins, tortoise shells, etc., or look into the matter carefully. You may be supporting the illegal trade in endangered species and, in fact, it may be illegal to import the product into Canada.

PART II

From NIMBY (Not In My Backyard) to NIMBI (Now I Must Become Involved)

Ultimately, Canadians will have the environment they deserve.
— Environment Canada, *Canada's Environment: An Overview*

There are over 25 million people in Canada and according to a recent poll, 94% are either somewhat or very concerned about the environment. This degree of consensus is unprecedented.

But given this agreement, why does environmental degradation continue? One reason may be that it is relatively easy to express concern to a pollster, but much more difficult to move from concern to action. What is it that holds us back? Simply a few often-repeated and untenable excuses:

• I'm not part of the problem.

We're all part of the problem and we can all be part of the solution.

• Environmental degradation doesn't affect me.

When you breathe it does.

• I'm too comfortable with the way things are and any changes will make my life less comfortable.

Our present comfort is short-term. The long-term effects of environmental degradation will cause unprecedented damage not only to North Americans' standard of living, but to the very existence of whole countries. If global warming continues and the sea level rises as the models predict, there are whole countries that will disappear under water. We are measuring our comfort in a fool's paradise that is destined to change — either through violent collapse or by acting now.

• Changing my habits is too difficult.

Either we change our habits now, voluntarily, or we will be forced to do so when reserves of fresh water, energy, productive soil, etc., are vastly reduced.

• The changes cost too much money.

Not acting and not making changes will cost the earth.

- **Even thinking about the necessary changes forces me to acknowledge the depressing state of the world. I'd rather not think about it.**

There is too much momentum behind most of the global environmental problems to hope that they'll even *slow down* without major changes to the ways that we do things. Closing our eyes and our minds to the problems is an ill-conceived luxury we can no longer afford.

- **The problems are too big. I can't possibly do anything about them.**

Why not? No one would say that a million people are not powerful. A group of a million people is just a collection of individuals.

- **Perhaps the government will make the necessary changes and I won't have to do anything.**

Individuals are responsible for their own actions. Unless we want governments to legislate everything — from the amount of water we are allowed to use to the temperature we heat our houses — we have to be responsible for our choices. The government does enact some environmental legislation, but most often this is in response to voter pressure. Encouraging governments to take responsible action does not mean we can absolve ourselves of environmental responsibility in our own lives.

- **What if I make the changes necessary and other people don't?**

What if everyone had this attitude?

We all have to act — now. We have to make fundamental changes to our habits, attitudes and expectations. It's not enough to express concern about the greenhouse effect, although concern is a start. The greenhouse effect is *caused* by us. Therefore the solution is with us.

According to the Worldwatch Institute, we have just ten years left to make the major changes that are necessary if we are to survive, if we are to leave a habitable planet to our children. *Ten years*. Think back to what you were doing ten years ago. Now try to think ahead. . . .

If you love this planet, prove it.

10

Home: Getting Our Own Houses in Order

The word *ecology* is based on the Greek *oikos*, which means home. However, the only home that we have — this planet — is rapidly being devastated by human activity. And as we destroy the planet, we are also destroying the home of millions of other species.

One way to start cleaning up our environment is to look at our own homes.

NON-TOXIC CLEANING ALTERNATIVES

Take a look underneath the kitchen sink, for example. Is this a haven for hazardous chemicals, a storehouse for poisons? Do any of the boxes, cans or jars under there have labels warning of the toxins inside? If your answer is "Yes," then you share with most Canadians the hazards of household cleaning materials.

Most of us use synthetic chemical cleaners because they are convenient: they save us time and energy. We buy a can and simply spray on miracles. Yet we rarely think of the other wonders they produce: with or without CFCs,

aerosols emit tiny droplets that lodge deep in the lungs; poisonous residues in some household cleaners may remain on surfaces; many products must be treated as hazardous wastes when discarded. In fact, hazardous wastes are produced twice: once when the chemical cleaners are manufactured and again when we use and dispose of them. Toxic chemicals end up in the sewage system (where not all are removed by the treatment), or directly in public waters if there is no sewage system; in landfill sites, where they may leach into the groundwater; or as toxic contaminants in the air, when they are incinerated.

However, there are alternatives.

The basic ingredients of most non-toxic household cleaners are just baking soda, borax, soap and vinegar. They can be combined, along with other ingredients, according to the recipes below, to produce safer and cheaper alternatives.

Although at first it might take just a bit more effort to use these recipes, remember that the environment is *not* bearing the cost, as it is with the short-lived convenience of the many chemical products on the market.

By making your own non-toxic household cleaners, not only will you limit your hazardous waste production, you will also help to solve the garbage problem. Instead of buying fifteen different "specialty" cleaners in fifteen different packages that get thrown out when they're empty, you can buy large packages of a few basic ingredients, mix them and store them in refillable containers.

The Basic Ingredients of "Environmentally Friendly" Cleaners

Baking Soda (sodium bicarbonate): A good all-purpose cleaner, with lots of scouring and polishing power. Can be used to soften water, to increase sudsing of soap. Also deodorizes.

White Vinegar: Cuts through grease, removes odour and prevents mould from growing.

Pure Soap: Available in a number of different forms: liquid, flakes, powder, bars. Example: *Ivory*. Buy unscented, uncoloured, pure soap, available in the laundry section of most grocery stores.

Washing Soda (sodium carbonate monohydrate): Cuts through grease, removes some stains. Also a water softener. Example: *Arm and Hammer*. Available in the laundry section of most grocery stores. Use in a well-ventilated area and protect skin with rubber gloves.

Borax (sodium borate): Cleans, deodorizes and disinfects. Removes some stains. Available in the laundry section of most grocery stores.

Household Ammonia: Cleans and disinfects. Use in a well-ventilated area; ammonia is caustic and can irritate skin and eyes. Use only when other cleaners can't do the job.

Cornstarch: Cleans, polishes and removes some stains.

Warning: *Never mix bleach and ammonia: toxic chloramine gas is produced. Never mix bleach and vinegar: toxic chlorine gas is produced.*

Recipes for Non-Toxic Cleaners

All-Purpose Cleaner
1 part baking soda
2 parts white vinegar
4 parts warm water

Place all ingredients together in a bucket and mix thoroughly. You can make up this cleaner as you need it, or you can make a larger batch and store it in a clean bottle. Hardware stores sell refillable pump spray bottles that make good applicators.

This produces a good general cleaner that will work on most surfaces.

Scouring Cleaner
Make a paste out of 1 part soap, 1 part baking soda and 2 parts warm water.
Apply by scrubbing with sponge or bristle brush.

Dishwashing Liquid or Powder
Use liquid or powdered pure soap (such as pure *Ivory* soap flakes). For greasy pots and pans, add a few tablespoons of white vinegar to the water.

Dishwasher Powder
1 part borax
1 part washing soda

If your water is hard, increase the amount of washing soda.

Dishwasher Phosphates

In the 1960s and 1970s, attention focussed on the fact that phosphates in detergent caused algae "blooms" in lakes and waterways. Federal regulations were introduced to limit the phosphate content in laundry detergents to 5%. However, because the use of automatic dishwashers was not as widespread as it is today, dishwasher detergents were exempt from the legislation. Consequently, they are often high in phosphates (some as high as 40%).

Oven Cleaner
Prevent spills by not overfilling pans or by placing a cookie sheet under cooking pans to catch accidental spills. If spills do occur, wipe up as soon as the oven is cool. For stubborn spills, use a paste of 1 part baking soda and 1 part water and scrub with steel wool.

Drain Cleaner
Prevent clogged drains by not pouring grease down the sink and always keeping the drain strainer in place. If the drain becomes clogged, pour 1 part baking soda and 2 parts vinegar down the drain and put in the plug. When the fizzing stops, flush with hot water. If the drain is still clogged, you may need to use a plunger or a plumber's snake. (Both are available from hardware stores.)

Window, Glass and Mirror Cleaners
Prepare a solution of pure soap and warm water in a bucket. Wash windows and then rinse with 1 part vinegar to 4 parts warm water. Wipe clean with crumpled newspapers to prevent streaking.

Mildew Cleaner
Mix 1 part borax with 1 part vinegar and use to wipe surfaces.

Carpet Cleaner
Clean stains or spills immediately by scrubbing with cold water or soda water. Mix 1 part borax with 2 parts cornmeal, sprinkle on the carpet and let sit for one hour. Vacuum.

Furniture Polish
Mix 1 part lemon juice with 2 parts vegetable or mineral oil. Apply to furniture with a rag and buff until dry.

Laundry Soap

Use pure soap flakes, adding washing soda to remove stains if necessary, or borax to soften hard water.

Fabric Softeners

Use 1/2 cup of vinegar in the rinse cycle. If you have problems with static in the dryer, you can either place a damp towel in with the load, or you can take clothes out of the dryer when slightly damp and hang to dry.

Air Fresheners

Commercial air fresheners work either by masking the smell or by coating the human nasal passage and temporarily deadening the sensory nerves. However, there are many alternatives. Baking soda reduces odours at their source (in the refrigerator or garbage can, for example). Houseplants and flowers can also refresh the air. When cooking pungent smelling foods, a bowl of warm vinegar on the stove should absorb odours. Boiling a pot of water with cinnamon or cloves will also mask odours.

To save time and effort, you may want to mix up a few different batches of cleaners that you often use and keep them well-sealed in pump spray bottles or containers. For example, you may have one bottle of all-purpose cleaner, one of window cleaner and one of dishwashing solution, all ready for use.

These are just a few suggestions of alternatives to chemical cleaning products. A number of environment groups have produced excellent pamphlets with many more ideas. Contact Friends of the Earth (which has produced a "Clean House, Clean Earth" kit), Pollution Probe and Greenpeace for detailed information on alternatives. See the source list for this chapter for books that provide non-toxic recipes for cleaners.

Clean and Conserve

There are a number of ways to reduce your use of disposable paper products:
• Shred old sheets and T-shirts to use as rags;
• Use newspapers instead of paper towels to wipe windows clean;
• Use sponges instead of disposable paper towels;
• Use washable and reusable cloth napkins at the table instead of paper serviettes.

If you are going to use store-bought cleaners, there are a number of precautions to keep in mind.

• Read the label. Is there a list of ingredients? Are you sure that these chemicals are not going to harm you, for example, if you breathe the fumes while cleaning, if the product leaves residues on surfaces, or if you ingest the product? Are you sure they won't harm the environment when disposed of? For information about the toxicity of cleaning products and possible health effects, contact your local hospital and ask for the toll-free number of the nearest poison control centre. For information about environmental effects, contact Friends of the Earth, Pollution Probe, Greenpeace or your provincial environment network for the name of a local environment group that can answer your questions.

• Is a safer product available? Is the company concerned about the environmental effects of the product? Try to buy your cleaning products at a health food store (where, in general, environmental concerns are integrated into buying policies) or ask the store manager at your grocery store to stock non-toxic products. Does the product contain phosphates? Does it biodegrade into environmentally harmless components? A number of companies produce non-toxic household cleaners: Shaklee Canada, La Balance, Nature Clean, Ecover, and Soap Factory, for example. If your supermarket does not carry non-toxic cleaning products, ask the manager to order them.

• Is the product available in a non-aerosol container? Propellants such as butane that are used in aerosols are released as fine droplets that can lodge deep in the lungs, and they are a source of indoor air pollution. Look for pump sprays, liquids or pastes instead.

• Buy chlorine-free products, if possible — for example, chlorine-free scouring powder and chlorine-free bleach. (Read labels to identify products *with* chlorine and avoid them.)

• Has the product been tested on animals? Some synthetic cleaning products are routinely tested on rats, rabbits and guinea pigs before being released for commercial use. However, it is possible to buy products that have not been tested on animals. The Toronto Humane Society's Animals in Research Coordinator Tita Zierer has produced a *Cruelty Free Shopper's Guide*, which lists the following household cleaners as *not* being tested on animals: *Bon Ami*, *Dr. Bonner's*, *Murphy's Oil Soap*, *Nature Clean*, *I. Rokeach & Sons*, *Soap Factory* and *Soap Works*. See the source list for organizations that provide information on which companies use animals in product research and which companies don't.

HOME CARE ALTERNATIVES

Painting
Although oil-based and alkyd paints may be necessary for outdoor paint jobs, it is best to substitute water-based latex paints wherever possible. Not only are water-based paints less

toxic (because they are thinned with water rather than with solvents), but they eliminate the need for clean-up with turpentine. For some jobs, you may be able to use non-toxic, limestone-based whitewash.

Some oil-based paints using natural tree resins rather than synthetic chemicals are available. teekah inc. is the exclusive Canadian distributor of the *AURO* line of West German paints, waxes, lacquers, oils and varnishes, which are made with natural, non-toxic substances. Contact teekah at 5015 Yonge Street, Willowdale, Ontario M2N 5P1; (416) 229-4199.

Livos is another line of natural, non-toxic wood finishing and home care products that are biodegradable and manufactured using natural and non-toxic ingredients. *Livos* products include wood stain finishes, paints, rust primer and wood preserver. Contact Livos Plant Chemistry Canada at P.O. Box 92, Apohaaqui, New Brunswick E0G 1A0; (506) 433-3455 for a catalogue.

If you are using oil-based paints, you can reuse the cleaning solvents and thinners. Once your brushes are clean, store the used solvent or thinner in a glass jar and the paint particles will eventually settle to the bottom. Carefully pour the clear liquid on top into another container and the solvent is ready for reuse.

Pests Inside the Home

The key to effective pest control is prevention: make sure that the pest does not get into the house in the first place. However, once you have a problem, you have to deal with it by first identifying the pest and then taking action to eliminate its supply of food, water and shelter. In this way, pests can be dealt with using biological or cultural controls that get right at the cause, rather than pesticides that deal only with symptoms (i.e., too many bugs).

Flies

Flies enter houses through open doors and unscreened windows. They breed in and feed on moist decaying matter, such as garbage. Remove this material at the source.

Use sticky flypaper (available at most hardware stores) to catch flies once they're inside.

Ants

Find out where the ants are entering the home, and place a line of talcum powder or charcoal dust at their point of entry.

Cockroaches

Cockroaches thrive in dark, moist places, so one way to eradicate them is to dehumidify any area that has an excessive amount of moisture or condensation. Never leave *any* food out and keep *all* surfaces spotless. Caulk any points of entry that cockroaches have (especially in apartments). Sprinkle a light dusting of borax around all baseboards and behind appliances (keep away from food surfaces and from pets). You can also try sprinkling diatomaceous earth (made of fossilized marine plants that puncture cockroach shells), which is sold commercially as *Fossil Flower* at most garden supply stores. Avoid inhaling. Setting cockroach traps, which can be found in most hardware stores, will control infestations but not eradicate the pest altogether.

Clothes Moths

Cupboards and closets should be dusted regularly, and aired out. At least once a year, shake out woollen clothing and hang it in sunlight for a few hours. Some people put cedar in their cupboards to prevent infestations, but there is no proof that this technique works.

A company called Safer, Inc. makes bio-degradable pesticides from natural, rather than synthetic, ingredients. The active ingredient is pyrethrum, made from a flower extract. Both the *Indoor Flea Guard* and *Timed Release Indoor-Outdoor Pest Control* made by Safer can be used to control pests inside the home.

For more information about pesticides and alternatives for household pests, see the source list for this chapter. In addition, the National Pesticide Information Service of Agriculture Canada will provide information on alternatives to pesticides in the home. Call 1-800-267-6315.

If you do resort to the use of a pest control company or to chemical pesticides, there are a number of precautions to follow.

• Use the alternatives listed above first.

• Shop around for a company that uses non-toxic control methods, such as diatomaceous earth. Tell the company that you are concerned about pesticides in the environment and their health effects, and that you want to use the least toxic control possible. Beware of companies that respond with comments like: "Pesticides are virtually harmless" or "I heard about someone who drank a cup of DDT for a year and nothing happened"! Look for a company that is aware of and honest about the dangers of pesticides and will act accordingly. There are companies that use non-toxic control methods, but you may have to make a few phone calls to find them. If you're having trouble locating a company in your area, call a local environment group or the city health department.

• If you are buying a pesticide for indoor use, read the label carefully. Make sure that the pest you are trying to control is listed on the label. Read the description of the product and the hazards associated with its use: you may want to reconsider your purchase!

• Follow the application directions to the letter. Do not use pesticides in any area where they may contaminate food, food surfaces, utensils or come in contact with pets. Cover all furniture and appliances.

• Pesticides are poisons. They can enter the body through the eyes, the mouth, the skin or through inhalation. If applying the pesticide yourself, protect yourself with a mask (ask at a hardware store or a safety supply store and tell them what you need the mask for) and thoroughly wash up afterwards (launder clothes in a separate wash).

- Store left-over pesticides, well sealed, in their original containers. Do not mix with other pesticides. Save containers for a hazardous waste collection day. Do not reuse pesticide containers and never burn empty containers.

- If an accidental spill does occur or you begin to feel ill after applying a pesticide, call your local hospital or poison control centre immediately.

HOUSEHOLD HAZARDOUS WASTES

The average Canadian household produces anywhere from 20 to 40 litres of hazardous wastes every year. If you use the alternatives already mentioned, you should be able to reduce the amount of hazardous wastes in your home significantly. This kind of source reduction is the best solution. However, there are some general guidelines that you should follow if you do use hazardous materials.

- Read labels and try to find the least toxic product available.

- Buy only what you need to do the job.

- Follow the directions on the label exactly. Use only the recommended amount.

- Use products in well-ventilated areas.

- Avoid aerosol products whenever possible. Fine particles of the propellant are released into the air with every use and they can lodge deep in the lungs.

- Keep products separate, securely capped and in their original containers.

- Store unused products in a safe place, away from children, animals and sources of ignition.

- Try to exchange your left-over products, such as paints, with neighbours or friends. (Windsor, Ontario, for example, had a paint exchange day in which 2,385 litres of paint were collected, mixed together and given away to people for use on picnic tables, chicken coops, etc. The demand for the free paint outstripped the supply!)

- Recycle used hazardous wastes. Phone your provincial environment ministry or local environment groups and ask where the nearest waste motor oil drop-off is. Car batteries may be traded in or given to service stations for recycling. Dentists may accept old thermometres for recycling of the mercury.

- A handy reference is available, the "Household Hazardous Waste Wheel," which outlines the toxins found in everyday materials, the non-toxic alternatives, and disposal recommendations. It is available from the Environmental Hazards Management Institute, 10 Newmarket Road, P.O. Box 932, Durham, New Hampshire 03801; (603) 868-1496.

Even after following the above suggestions, you will find that many household products still require special disposal. Take a broken wristwatch, for example. If burned, the batteries in some watches emit toxic lead, cadmium, mercury and chromium. Some smoke detectors contain radioactive materials. Moreover, PCBs can be found in the capacitors of older fluorescent lamps. The most important thing to remember is that these materials are hazardous and require special disposal:

• Don't pour hazardous wastes down the drain. They can release toxic fumes, harm the necessary microbes in the sewage treatment process, and contaminate surface and groundwater.

• Don't put hazardous wastes out with your regular garbage. They are special wastes and they require special action.

• Don't burn or bury hazardous wastes. They will release toxic gases into the air or contaminate soil and groundwater.

Disposing of Hazardous Wastes

• Find out if your community has a hazardous waste pick-up service by phoning your provincial environment ministry or your local public works department. Save your hazardous wastes for pick-up.

• If your community does not have a hazardous waste pick-up service, find out if there is a special waste depot or a permanent drop-off site where you can take your hazardous wastes.

• If there are no provisions for dealing with hazardous wastes, try to avoid buying any hazardous material that you can't dispose of or recycle. Write letters and talk with local politicians about the need for hazardous waste collection. Support environment groups working on hazardous waste disposal issues.

11 Garbage: Trim That Tonne

Each Canadian produces approximately one tonne of household waste every year. We can start reducing the amount of garbage we throw out by looking at what's in that tonne. Most of our household garbage is not really garbage at all, but rather reusable, recyclable materials.

WHAT'S RECYCLABLE?

Newspapers

Many municipalities pick up newspapers for recycling. Some have permanent recycling depots where individuals can drop off newspapers.

By recycling just one newspaper each day for a year, you will be contributing about 140 kg of post-consumer waste to the recycled paper production process, thereby saving:

- approximately 2.5 trees;
- over 50% of the energy required to produce an equal amount of paper from virgin wood pulp;
- 60% of the water needed to manufacture virgin paper;

- 35% of the water pollution that results from the virgin paper production process;
- 75% of the air pollution that results from the production process.

It is important to keep your batches of newspaper for recycling free of other materials. For example, glossy colour magazines will "contaminate" the batch and some recycling companies will reject the whole load.

Fine Paper

Although most municipalities do not collect fine paper (e.g., writing or computer paper) in their Blue Box programs, it can be recycled. Contact your provincial recycling council and ask where you can take fine paper to be recycled.

Cans

Rinse cans and put them out in your Blue Box or take them to a recycling depot. You do not have to remove labels.

Bottles

You can reuse bottles in the home for storing other items, or you can give them a quick rinse and put them out for recycling. Do not contaminate your recyclable glass by including non-recyclable materials such as pieces of broken plates or mirrors.

Although you do not have to remove labels, you should remove caps and plastic rings.

Plastics

Recycling of plastics is only now becoming more common. The plastics industry is researching and experimenting with various processes and some municipalities are accepting plastics in their Blue Box programs.

Food Wastes

Most food wastes can be "recycled" through composting. The nutrient-rich, decomposed material can be used to improve the soil in the yard or garden. (See Composting section below.)

Blue Box Tips

- Put your Blue Box out for pick-up only when it is full. This will help the recycling system to work efficiently.

- If you're not sure what can go in your Blue Box, you can:
  — phone your provincial recycling council;
  — phone the local public works department;
  — let the collector decide; if the material is not acceptable, in some cities the collector will leave the item in your Blue Box.

- Take note of materials that are not covered by the program and buy only those materials that are.

The major components of most household garbage *can* be recycled. Once you know what materials make up your garbage and how many of them can be recycled, you are well on the way to trimming that tonne.

Recycling is just one method of reducing the waste stream and it is a method that deals only with end-products. The most effective way to deal with excess garbage is to attack the problem at its source: that is, *reduce* the amount of garbage you throw away.

• Don't buy overpackaged products. You can go even further by letting store managers and manufacturers know why you are refusing overpackaged goods. If enough people use their power as consumers to reject overpackaging, the message will get through to manufacturers.

When is a product overpackaged?

• When the package can't be recycled because it's made out of a number of different materials (for example, many boxed drink packages).
• When a product is packaged in "single serving" units (for example, microwave dinners or the sugar and ketchup packages in fast-food restaurants).
• When the product is packaged for convenience without concern for the environment (take-out foods in foam containers, for example).
• When the product is "bulked up" with packaging in order to make it seem like more value for money (many cosmetics and toys, for example).

Say "No" to excess packaging because:

• When dumped, it fills up landfill sites;
• When burned, it releases pollutants;
• It wastes energy and resources;
• You're paying for the hidden costs of packaging with the product;
• You're paying again for municipal waste disposal;
• You can't eat packaging.

Source (for "Say 'No'" list): Ontario Public Interest Research Group, *Factsheet on Waste Management*

- Buy in bulk whenever possible. Pass up the foam container of fruit, for example, and buy in bulk instead.
- Buy one large container rather than a number of smaller ones.
- Buy beverages in returnable containers.
- Buy a "Born to be Recycled" mug from the Recycling Council of Ontario and use it for take-out coffee instead of disposable cups.
- Buy durable items rather than disposables.

Keep your "Born to be Recycled" mug handy: reduce your use of disposable cups and spread the message.

Source: Recycling Council of Ontario

Durability versus Planned Obsolescence

Planned obsolescence, the ultimate manipulation of consumer confidence, goes against everything that durability stands for, without actually wearing the disposable label. Planned obsolescence can take many forms, from the psychological technique of giving car models a year — so that the 1989 model is "out of date" by the time the 1990 model is introduced — to building failure right into the product, so that replacement is necessary.

Manufacturers and marketers have come up with some creative euphemisms for planned obsolescence:

- economic stimulation;
- controllable wear;
- pre-determined life span;
- planned existence;
- limited-life economics;
- balancing product's life with length of warranty.

Perhaps the most revealing, though, is "organized waste" — waste is exactly what is being manufactured and marketed in products that are designed *not* to last. The alternative is clear — buy for durability.

- Disposable diapers account for approximately 2.4 to 3% of all solid waste in Canada — that's over 200,000 tonnes a year. Not only do the sheer numbers give this convenience item a high cost in terms of environmental impact but, in fact, what most people do with disposable diapers — throw them out — is actually illegal. Human biological waste is not permitted in landfill because the viruses and contaminants can leach into water and soil. (The small print on some disposable diaper packages suggests that you flush the waste in the toilet before disposing of the diaper.)

However, there is a convenient alternative to disposable diapers, one that is cheaper in terms of environmental cost and even cheaper to the consumer — cloth diaper services. (Of course, it is even cheaper to buy diapers and wash them at home. Contact the cloth diaper service in your area to find out where you can buy cloth diapers.)

Cloth diapers may also be better for a baby's health. According to one study, they are three times less likely to cause diaper rash and they don't contain the synthetic chemicals found in disposable diapers.

A list of cloth diaper services appears in the source list for this chapter. Contact a local environment group, your local hospital or your doctor, or consult the yellow pages under "Diaper Services" if you are having trouble finding a service in your area.

An excellent booklet, *Alternatives in Diapering*, is available from 5015-46 Street, Camrose, Alberta T4V 3G3; (403) 672-1763.

THINK RE-USE RATHER THAN REFUSE

Another way to reduce the amount of garbage in the bin is to reuse materials. For example, take your own carrying bags to the store and reuse them every shopping trip. A small business in Ottawa makes attractive 100% cotton, durable shopping bags: contact Earthbags, P.O. Box 6730, Station J, Ottawa, Ontario K2A 3Z4; (613) 596-1816.

Think of other people who might be able to use the things you've finished with. For example, some hospitals accept used magazines. The Salvation Army refurbishes and resells old appliances.

Composting

A typical Canadian household produces one-third of a tonne of food waste every year. Most of this material is not waste at all, but potential fertilizer for the yard and garden.

Organic materials are broken down naturally by bacteria and fungi. Composting speeds up this process by providing an optimum environment for the transformation of organic wastes to the nutrient-rich end-product: humus.

Composting is a bit like cooking: you combine a number of ingredients, stir them around and leave them to simmer for a while. What you end up with is an earth-smelling soil conditioner. The whole process takes anywhere from weeks to months, depending on the composition of the pile, and can be done in a corner of the yard or even on a balcony.

What You Need in Order to Compost

- Soil, moisture and air.

- A supply of food and/or yard wastes, i.e., organic material.

- A corner of the yard or garden in which to make the compost heap. The size of the heap will depend on the amount of material you're going to add to it.

- You can buy a composter, but can make compost that is just as satisfactory either by building a makeshift wooden box for the compost heap, or just keeping it as an unenclosed pile. If you are going to build a structure, make sure that you leave spaces between the boards to allow for the movement of air.

Benefits of Composting

- Reduces the amount of garbage going to landfill sites or garbage incinerators.

- Adds moisture to soil and improves soil structure.

- Adds nutrients to soil.

How to Compost

- It takes very little work to get a compost heap *going*, i.e., decomposing. All you do is alternate layers of food and garden scraps with a thin dusting of soil, keeping the mixture moist and turning it every 1 to 3 weeks with a pitchfork or shovel.

- The smaller the pieces of food or yard waste, the faster the decomposition will be. If you want to produce compost quickly, chop up food waste into pieces about 1 cm long.

- Although composting slows right down in the winter, you can continue to add organic materials. It's fine if your heap freezes, although if you want the decomposition process to continue throughout the winter, put an insulating layer of plastic over the heap.

Carried Away by Compost

Gardeners tend to become poetic about compost. Take the editors of *Organic Gardening* magazine, for example:

"The entire composting process, awesome in its contribution to all plant and animal life, is probably impossible to contemplate."

What Should and Should Not Go on the Compost Heap

Should
Yard Wastes: grass clippings, dead leaves, shredded twigs and branches, flower cuttings, pruned material.

Food Wastes: all fruits, vegetables, grains, eggs, baked goods, tea bags, coffee grounds.

Should Not
Yard Wastes: roots of hardy weeds (such as knotweed), dog or cat faeces, diseased plants.

Food Wastes: meat, bones, highly fatty foods such as salad dressing (these materials will compost, but they may attract animals).

Paper Wastes: colour comics, newspapers (some of the inks may contain lead and cadmium), large amounts of wood ash (which may contain concentrated heavy metals).

Plastics, cans, glass, and any toxic materials such as household cleaners, motor oil, etc.

General Tips
- Turning your compost heap (exposing the buried material to the air) will speed up the composting process and keep the heap from giving off odours. The heap should be turned every 1 to 3 weeks.

- Build your heap on a well-drained site.

- A compost heap should be as moist as a squeezed sponge.

- If your heap begins to smell, it may not be getting enough oxygen or may be too moist and compacted. Turn the materials over with a pitchfork or shovel.

- The carbon-nitrogen ratio determines the speed at which your pile decomposes. The optimum carbon-nitrogen ratio for quick composting is from 25:1 to 30:1. Alternate layers of high and low nitrogen-containing materials, and try to compensate for high carbon materials with high nitrogen materials: lawn clippings and rotted manure. Adding phosphorous (in the form of bone meal, fish meal or rock phosphate) will help to conserve nitrogen in the heap.

- Cover your heap in winter to keep it well insulated.

- If you don't want an exposed compost heap, you can use a large garbage can, but punch holes on the side to allow for adequate aeration.

- Commercial composters are available at most garden centres. Some municipalities have special programs in which they sell commercial composters at a reduced rate in order to encourage people to compost.

- Apartment dwellers can use commercial composters to make compost on balconies, which can then be used for indoor houseplants.

What To Do With Compost
- You can tell that your compost is ready by checking its structure (it should be crumbly rather than lumpy), its colour (dark brown), and its odour (like earth).

- Work compost into soil for a general conditioner. It can be added to gardens and lawns throughout the growing season.

- Compost can be used for starting seedlings in peat pots in the spring. Mix 1 part compost with 1 part soil.

Where is the Biggest Compost Heap in Canada?

The village of Ryley, in Alberta, must have the largest multi-material compost heap in the country. Ninety-five percent of the residents save organic wastes from the yard and kitchen and put them out for special collection. In this way, one-third of the residents' garbage is diverted from landfill and sent for composting instead. Each year, the town distributes from 30 to 100 tonnes of free compost.

Metro Toronto has one of the biggest leaf composting operations in North America. In the fall of 1988, over 7,000 tonnes of leaves were collected in East York, the City of York and the City of Toronto. The leaves were composted and used for parks and landfill cover.

If you have any questions about composting, your provincial recycling council should be able to help you. The council may also provide instruction sheets on how to build your own compost container. In addition, you can contact the Canadian Organic Growers for advice; they publish an excellent fact sheet on composting. The Ecological Agriculture Project also publishes an information-filled fact sheet on composting. (See source list for addresses.)

12 Energy: Turning On Efficiency

During the 1970s, energy conservation was a popular idea — the energy "crisis" forced governments to encourage the public to use energy wisely, to become less wasteful, to *think* about energy consumption. Government programs sprang up, research into alternative energy sources was financed, and individuals tried to make a difference.

Somehow though, with the *immediate* crisis over (even though longer term crises, such as global warming, were becoming more apparent), all that changed in the 1980s. Government spending on alternative energy was slowly eroded, conservation programs started to drop out of sight and, at the same time, spending on massive oil development projects continued to grow.

The result: of all the world's industrially developed countries, Canada is said to have the highest per capita energy consumption, and approximately 80% of that energy is from fossil fuels such as coal and oil. Put simply,

Canadians use more energy (and therefore contribute more to global warming) than any other people on earth.

According to the World Bank's 1986 figures, each Canadian uses the equivalent of 8,945 kg of oil per year. The annual average for industrial market economies is 4,952 kg of oil per person; the average for developing countries, 506 kg.

Some of our high energy use can be attributed to our climate (although Canada is just one northern country and others manage to use less energy), some to our resource-based economy (industries require large amounts of energy to process and transport raw materials) and some to our lower population density (making it necessary to transport goods long distances).

However, as the 1970s "crisis" showed, energy consumption is directy related to perceived energy availability and relatively low costs. As long as we believe that we have an endless supply, and as long as we ignore the environment when counting the cost of that energy supply, we are living (albeit comfortably) under a delusion — a delusion that is the direct cause of major environmental degradation.

THE THREE ENERGY OPTIONS

I'm not suggesting that we have to go around in overcoats with thermostats set at zero, but we simply must be more energy efficient.
— former Environment Minister Tom McMillan, in *Maclean's*, September 5, 1988

There are three energy options available to slow down and eventually stop the environmental catastrophes that go along with our current energy consumption:

• energy efficiency;
• energy conservation;
• alternative energy sources.

Using energy efficiently means getting the greatest possible use out of each energy unit. For example, some brands and models of appliances are more energy efficient than others.

Energy can be conserved by using less to begin with, and using it more efficiently. Although conservation usually conjures up images of "doing without," it is really just a matter of "doing differently" — for example, walking three blocks to the store instead of driving.

The two principles of conservation and efficiency can be immediately and effectively embraced by each and every Canadian. However, what is ultimately needed is a massive shift from non-renewable and polluting sources

of energy (such as oil and coal) to renewable and environmentally benign energy sources. This shift has to occur at an institutional and political level; in other words, governments have to make a commitment to alternative energy: they have to fund research and institute policies that ensure alternative energy use.

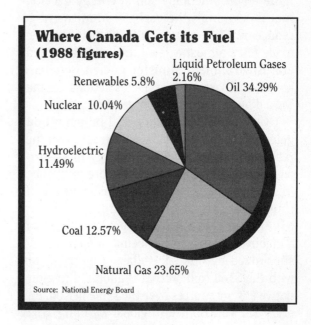

Where Canada Gets its Fuel (1988 figures)

- Liquid Petroleum Gases 2.16%
- Oil 34.29%
- Renewables 5.8%
- Nuclear 10.04%
- Hydroelectric 11.49%
- Coal 12.57%
- Natural Gas 23.65%

Source: National Energy Board

Renewable Energy Sources

Renewable energy is based on resources that are continuously available and that regenerate themselves over a period of time. For example:

Solar Power: Capturing and using the heat from the sun.

Tidal Power: Harnessing energy from the ocean.

Geothermal Power: Using the steam and hot water from the earth's crust to generate power.

Wind Power: Harnessing energy from wind.

Biomass: Using plant sources to produce energy.

What is the federal government doing to promote environmentally sound energy development? Although the verbal commitment to reduce our dependence on fossil fuels has been made ("It's almost a revolution we need," federal Environment Minister Lucien Bouchard has claimed), the government's actions are taking a different direction altogether.

Over the next four years, $5.1 billion is budgeted for loans and grants to extract fossil fuel resources. Non-renewable energy mega-projects such as the Hibernia offshore oil project in Newfoundland, the Lloydminster heavy oil upgrader, the OSLO oil sands project in Alberta and the natural gas pipeline on Vancouver Island are all being supported and subsidized by our tax dollars. Compare this with the $160 million that is allocated to alternative energy sources over the same period. For every $32 contributed to global warming, $1 is contributed to non-polluting energy sources of the future.

One way to encourage the government to divert money away from polluting fossil fuel development and into environmentally sound alternatives is to take a vocal stand on the issue.

- Write to your provincial energy minister to support renewable energy technologies. (See source list for addresses.)

- For more information on Canada's energy policies and the potential of alternative forms of renewable energy, contact one or more of the many groups working on these issues. (See source list for addresses.)

- Energy Probe is one of Canada's major non-governmental energy watchdog organizations. Two of its objectives are "to educate Canadians to the benefits of conservation and renewable energy and to help Canadians achieve long-term energy self-sufficiency in the shortest possible time, with the fewest disruptive effects, and with the greatest societal, environmental and economic benefits." Contact Energy Probe for a list of their publications; their work is funded entirely by donations.

- Friends of the Earth has produced an excellent analysis of the federal government's cuts to energy conservation and renewable energy programs, placing these cuts within the context of the greenhouse effect. *Demolishing the Fire Hall* is available from Friends of the Earth. The group has also launched a major campaign, "Escaping the Heat Trap," to promote sustainable energy policies. Write for more information and send in a donation.

- *The Canadian Energy Education Directory* (updated annually) lists hundreds of organizations in Canada that are active in the field of energy education. It also lists the kinds of education programs available for use in schools. For a free copy of the directory, write to the Alberta Department of Energy, Energy

Conservation Branch, Highfield Place, 2nd Floor, 10010-106 Street, Edmonton, Alberta T5J 3L8; (403) 427-5200.

- The Alberta Department of Energy operates the "Energy Matters Database," which is a telephone inquiry service with both general and technical information on a wide range of energy topics, from solar energy to maximum efficiency house design to water conservation. In Alberta, dial 0 and ask for Zenith 22339; in other provinces, call (403) 427-5300.

- For information on solar energy and where to find solar-energy products, contact the Solar Energy Society of Canada. The Society has chapters throughout Canada; check your telephone directory for the local group. (See source list for address of headquarters.) The Society also publishes Canada's solar energy magazine, *Sol*. For product information, you can also contact the Canadian Solar Industries Association. The CSIA publishes a manual on how to install a solar hot water heater in your home.

- The Canadian Wind Energy Association has published a bilingual booklet, *Wind Energy*, which provides information on using wind-power in the industrial and commercial sectors.

- For information on biomass energy, contact the Biomass Energy Institute or the Canadian Wood Energy Institute.

- For information on nuclear energy, contact Energy Probe; the Canadian Coalition for Nuclear Responsibility; Greenpeace; and Nuclear Awareness Project. The Nuclear Awareness Project publishes a critique of nuclear power in their *Nuclear Power Booklet*. Energy Probe has published two information packages on the nuclear power/nuclear weapons connection: *Canada's International Nuclear Trade: Development Issues* and *Canada's International Nuclear Trade: The Economics and Weapons Connections*. Contact Public Citizen (see below) for their publications list, particularly their documentation of American nuclear power plant accidents.

- An American group, Public Citizen, has many pamphlets, brochures, articles and publications available on energy topics. Their report, *Turning Down the Heat: Solutions to Global Warming*, is an excellent analysis of energy issues.

- Check with your provincial environment network to find out what groups in your area are working on promoting alternate energy sources. There are many groups across the country.

TURNING ON ENERGY EFFICIENCY IN YOUR OWN HOME

Appliances can consume up to 25% of the total energy used in the home, so a good place to start "turning on efficiency" is with household appliances.

The key to energy efficiency is the Energuide label, which can be found on all new appliances sold in Canada. This label outlines the amount of energy used by the appliance; the lower the Energuide rating, the more efficient the appliance.

When buying a new refrigerator, dryer or any other major purchase, you're also committing yourself to the cost of running the appliance. This cost is sometimes called the second price tag. By using the Energuide label to calculate which appliance will be cheapest to *run*, you can save money *and* energy.

Calculating the Second Price Tag

The Energuide label tells you how many kilowatt hours (kWh) per month the appliance uses. For example, when shopping for a freezer, you may have the choice between an energy-efficient model that uses 45 kWh of electricity per month and costs $400 and a similar model that costs just $300 but uses 80 kWh of electricity per month.

By using the following formula to calculate the second price tag, you'll see that the model with the higher purchase price but lower Energuide rating actually costs *less* than the apparently cheaper model. However, the lower long-term cost is not the only consideration: you are, above all, using less energy, burning less fossil fuels to create that energy, and therefore contributing less to global warming, acid rain and resource depletion. These are the *real* savings.

Formula to calculate the second price tag: Energuide rating (kWh/month) × 12 months in the year × the appliance life in years × local electricity cost (dollars per kWh; phone your local utility company for a figure) = estimated cost to run the appliance over its lifetime.

To compare the second price tags of the freezers in our example, the life of both appliances is estimated to be 21 years; the cost of electricity is estimated at $0.055 per kWh.

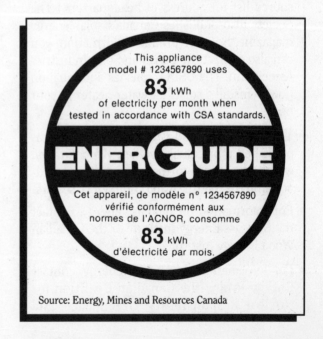

This appliance model # 1234567890 uses **83** kWh of electricity per month when tested in accordance with CSA standards.

EnerGuide

Cet appareil, de modèle n° 1234567890 vérifié conformément aux normes de l'ACNOR, consomme **83** kWh d'électricité par mois.

Source: Energy, Mines and Resources Canada

Calculation for the more efficient freezer (45 kWh/month on Energuide label):

45 kWh × 12 × 21 × 0.055 = $623.70

Calculation for the less efficient freezer (80 kWh/month on Energuide label):

80 kWh × 12 × 21 × 0.055 = $1,108.80

Thus, by buying the more efficient freezer, you are saving $485.10 in energy costs over the life of the appliance. Even if you take the higher initial price tag into account, you are saving $385.10.

Estimated Life Expectancy of Appliances:

(Use to calculate the second price tag)

Dishwasher: 13 years
Clothes Washer: 14 years
Clothes Dryer: 18 years
Refrigerator: 17 years
Freezer: 21 years
Electric Stove: 18 years

Source: Energy, Mines and Resources Canada, *Consumer's Guide to Buying Energy Efficient Appliances and Lighting*

Buying Efficiency

The following list shows the kilowatt hours per month of both the most efficient and the least efficient models. The calculations that follow are based on the same up-front cost for both models, on an average electricity cost of $0.055 per kWh, and on the life expectancies of appliances shown above.

Frost-free Refrigerator (440-510 litres):

Most efficient: 73 kWh/month
Least efficient: 145 kWh/month

Amount saved by buying the most efficient model: $808.00

Freezer (280-400 litres):

Most efficient: 42 kWh/month
Least efficient: 82 kWh/month

Amount saved: $554

Stove:

Most efficient: 62 kWh/month
Least efficient: 75 kWh/month

Amount saved: $154

Dishwasher:

Most efficient: 83 kWh/month
Least efficient: 121 kWh/month

Amount saved: $326

Clothes Washer (60-80 litres):

Most efficient: 50 kWh/month
Least efficient: 128 kWh/month

Amount saved: $721

Clothes Dryer (140-170 litres):

Most efficient: 81 kWh/month
Least efficient: 111 kWh/month

Amount saved: $356

Buying and Maintaining Appliances for Energy Efficiency

Refrigerators

Buying
Although the Energuide label indicates average energy use, there are a few other guidelines to keep in mind when buying a refrigerator:

- Generally, one-door manual-defrost models use less energy than two-door, automatic defrost refrigerators.

- Frills such as a butter conditioner (actually a small heater inside the refrigerator!) or a crushed ice dispenser increase energy use.

- Buy the size of refrigerator that fits your needs. If you buy one that is too large, you're wasting money and electricity cooling wasted space.

Maintenance and Use
- To work efficiently, refrigerators need to be installed properly. They need adequate air space (a minimum of 2.5 cm on each side and 10 cm on top), and should not be too close to heat sources such as stoves, dishwashers or heat vents.

- A good temperature setting is 3°C for the food compartment and -10°C for the freezer. A setting of just 4°C colder can increase energy use by as much as 10%.

- Coils (on the back of most refrigerators) should be cleaned at least twice a year. Unplug the appliance first and then vacuum or dust the coils.

- Check to see that the door seal is working by closing the door with a small piece of paper half in and half out. If you can pull the paper out easily, the seal should be replaced.

- Freezer compartments work better when they are almost full. Fill up empty space with bags of ice.

- Freezers work most efficiently when there is no build-up of frost. Do not allow ice to build up beyond 0.5 cm.

- Put frozen foods in the refrigerator to thaw. They will help to cut down the amount of electricity needed to keep the refrigerator cool.

- Allow hot foods to cool to room temperature before putting them in the refrigerator.

Freezers

Buying

- In general, of the two kinds of freezers available — chest and upright — chest freezers are more energy-efficient. Cold air may leak from the door of upright freezers, and more cold air rushes out when you open the door.

Maintenance and Use

- Check the door seal using the method outlined for refrigerators.

- Consult the owner's manual to determine the correct clearance or air space needed by the freezer.

Stoves

Buying

- Although the Energuide label will give you the energy rating, in general, self-cleaning ovens are better insulated than regular ranges and therefore require less energy to cook food.

- Energuide ratings are not provided for gas ranges, but it is best to get one with an electronic ignition rather than a pilot light. Pilot lights burn gas at all times.

- Microwave ovens use approximately half the amount of energy that standard ranges do. Convection ovens, too, generally save energy by cooking food in a shorter period at lower temperatures. However, some models are poorly insulated, so the energy savings are lost. Shop around for a well-insulated model.

Maintenance and Use

- Keep surface elements clean, but don't line drip pans with aluminum foil (this can damage the element).

- When using a self-cleaning oven, clean only when necessary and always after cooking, so that you use the heat already generated.

- When cooking, use pots that fit the element and lids that fit the pots. The bottom of the pot should cover the element.

- When boiling, use the minimum amount of water needed. Once it reaches a boil, turn the heat down to the lowest setting needed to keep it boiling.

- In general, glass baking dishes transfer heat more effectively than metal pans. If using heat-treated glass, you can reduce the oven temperature by approximately 14°C.

- Open the oven door as seldom as possible when baking; look through the window to check on food instead. (As much as 20% of the oven's heat can be lost with each opening.)

- Use appliances other than the stove to get jobs done. For example, toasting bread in a toaster uses a third of the energy used by a stove to do the same job; an electric kettle uses half of the energy needed by the stove to boil the same amount of water.

- If using a gas stove, the flame should be clear and blue-coloured. If there are yellow or orange streaks in the flame, something may be clogging the outlet. Try cleaning the burner with a toothpick or pipe cleaner, and if the flame is still streaked with yellow or orange, call the gas company for service (usually free).

Dishwashers

Buying
- Buy a dishwasher with an energy-saving option, sometimes called a short cycle option, which uses less hot water than the normal cycle. Some models have switches so that you can turn off the electric-dry cycle and allow the dishes to air dry.

- To work effectively, most dishwashers require that your hot water tank be set at 60°C. However, if you have lowered your tank to 55°C to save energy, you may want to buy a dishwasher that has a booster heater or "sani" setting that will bring the temperature of the water up to 60°C.

Maintenance and Use
- Use the energy-saving cycle. If you scrape plates and dishes before putting them in the dishwasher, this cycle will clean effectively.

- Wash only full loads.

- You may be able to stop your dishwasher before the drying cycle begins. Do so if you can, open the door and let the dishes air dry.

Clothes Washers

Buying
- Look for a washing machine that has a cold wash and cold rinse option, which will allow you to reduce hot water consumption. Some machines also have variable water level control, so that you can adjust the water level for small loads.

Maintenance and Use
- Use your washing machine only with full loads, but be careful not to overload it.

- You can use the cold rinse for every load of laundry, although you may want to experiment using the cold wash with different fabrics and colours.

- After the spin cycle, hang up clothes instead of using the dryer.

- Clean the filter on the water hose inlet at the back of your machine regularly.

Clothes Dryers

Buying
- Some dryers have built-in sensors that automatically turn off the machine when clothes are dry.

- Some machines also have a permapress setting, in which no heat is used for the last few minutes of the cycle.

Maintenance and Use
- Clean out the lint filter before turning on the dryer.

- Twice a year, clean out the lint built up in the exhaust hose, exhaust pipe and vent. Check the damper for obstructions.

- Do not overdry clothes. Clothes that need ironing can be ironed when damp. Consider using a clothes line outside in the summer.

Air Conditioners

Buying
- Read Chapter 3, "Losing the Ozone Layer," before you buy an air conditioner.

- Instead of buying an air conditioner, you can try to avoid the three main causes of heat build-up in the summer: direct sunlight through windows, heat from lights and appliances, and heat gain from the attic. Keep drapes closed, use as few appliances as possible and ventilate the attic.

- If you do buy an air conditioner, choose the model with the lowest Energuide rating.

Maintenance and Use
- Install the air conditioner away from direct sunlight. If this is not possible, place a canopy or awning over the window to shade the unit.

- Air conditioners work much harder when there is a lot of humidity in the air. Keep indoor humidity down by using a fan in the bathroom and kitchen.

- Close vents to the basement, as it will stay cool without the air conditioner.

- If the night is cool, turn off the air conditioner and open the windows for fresh air.

- In the spring and again in the fall, vacuum the coils and clean or replace the filter.

T.V. Sets: Another Reason to Call Them "Idiot Boxes"

According to the energy experts at the Rocky Mountain Institute in Colorado, most new television sets use from 1.5 to 8 watts of standby power (for the remote control) *when they are turned off*. This means that a 1,000-megawatt power plant (equal to 1/750th of the total U.S. power plant capacity) must run continuously in order to power all of the television sets in the United States when they are not even on.

Source: Rocky Mountain Institute

For more information on buying appliances or using them efficiently, contact:

- Energy, Mines and Resources Canada. They have produced many free guides and pamphlets on energy efficiency. They also produce the *Energuide Directory,* which contains information on the Energuide label. (See the blue pages in the phone book for your regional office.)

- Your provincial ministry of energy. (See blue pages or source list.)

- Your local utility company. (Check your utility bill.)

- The American Council for an Energy-Efficient Economy has produced a booklet, *Saving Energy and Money With Home Appliances,* that is available from the ACEE, 1001 Connecticut Avenue, Suite 535, Washington, D.C. 20036.

Efficient Lighting

- Fluorescent lights use less energy than regular incandescent lights. Many people do not like the quality of light they cast but there are new types of compact fluorescent bulbs that produce light comparable to incandescent and use 70 to 80% less energy. They can be added to ordinary light fixtures with an adapter. Ask for them in any hardware or lighting store. Although the initial cost will be higher, the longer life of fluorescent bulbs and lower energy use do make them cheaper in the long run.

- In general, fixtures that use a single incandescent bulb use less energy: for example, 6 25-watt bulbs are needed to produce the light of a single 100-watt bulb.

- Use low wattage bulbs in areas where strong lighting is not needed.

- Install dimmer switches so that you can adjust light level, save energy and extend the life of the bulb.

- Turn off lights when you don't need them, even if you are leaving a room for just a few minutes.

- Use task lights (lamps that provide localized light) when doing close work such as reading.

- Don't waste electricity by lighting up the outdoors. Leave on only those outdoor lights that are required for safety and turn off lights used for decoration.

13

Energy Conservation in the Home

Conservation does not mean being cold and uncomfortable in your home in winter! Instead, it means making sensible changes to your use of energy, changes that save you money and save valuable resources.

The major components of an energy conserving household are insulation, airtight construction, controlled ventilation, passive solar heating (i.e., taking advantage of the heat from the sun) and an efficient heating system. Basically, the house is designed and maintained to minimize heat loss and to maximize the use of passive solar heating and the home's own heating system.

The benefits of an energy-efficient home are many. Energy conservation is an investment in the future — by using less fossil fuels, you are conserving resources. In financial terms, heating bills are lower and you save money. But there are also benefits in terms of comfort: an energy-efficient house has even temperature distribution; therefore, it will feel warmer at lower temperature settings in winter and will also feel cooler in summer.

INSULATING AND CONTROLLING VENTILATION

Stopping Air Leakage

Air leakage generally accounts for as much as 40% of a home's heat loss. Although good ventilation is extremely important, you should be able to control that ventilation, rather than depending on leaks and cracks for fresh air.

Check a number of general problem areas when looking for air leaks. If you can feel air movement with the back of your hand along windows, doors, baseboards, electrical outlets, fireplaces or vent ducts, it means that heat can escape. (You can also use a feather to test for leaks.)

Air leaks can be sealed using a number of different methods.

Weatherstripping

Weatherstripping is used to minimize air leakage around moveable joints such as the moving parts of windows, doors or attic hatches. You can find weatherstripping in any hardware store and it is usually sold with installation instructions.

Where to install weatherstripping
- Around door frames, at the seal where the door meets the frame;
- Around window frames, at the seal where the window meets the sill;
- Around storm windows;
- Around the attic hatch, where the trap door shuts.

Caulking
Caulking is used to control air leakage around permanent or fixed joints. You can find caulking at any hardware store; it is usually sold as a tube of semi-liquid material that you can apply with a caulking gun.

Where to use caulking
- Around baseboards, where the floor meets the baseboard and where the wall meets the baseboard;
- Where door and window frames meet the walls;
- Around ceiling light fixtures;
- Around electrical outlets.

General Tips to Minimize Air Leakage
- Close up the mail slot in the door, seal well and replace with an outside mail box.
- Block drafts from underneath doors with a "snake." Snakes are available from some spe-

cialty stores or you can make your own by rolling up some bulky fabric and sewing the tube together. Place at the bottom of doors.

- Take the switch plate off of electrical outlets (turn off the power first!) and place a foam gasket between the electrical box and the switch plate. (Foam gaskets are available at many hardware stores. They have the same shape as the switch plate.)
- Seal any unused keyholes.

Insulation
To prevent heat loss, houses should be well insulated. However, it is not necessarily true that the thicker the insulation, the better it is. Rather, insulation is rated according to its "thermal resistance value," or its RSI value, which measures the resistance of the insulation to heat loss. The higher the RSI number, the better the material insulates.

In general, the areas of the house that require insulation are the walls, basement, roof or attic, and the floor (over unheated areas). The minimum amount of insulation needed is outlined in the National Building Code, and it varies throughout the country.

Checking Your Insulation

Attic
- Look for evenly distributed insulation, with no spaces between insulation batts.
- Insulation should not block the ventilation at the eaves.

Insulation Zones

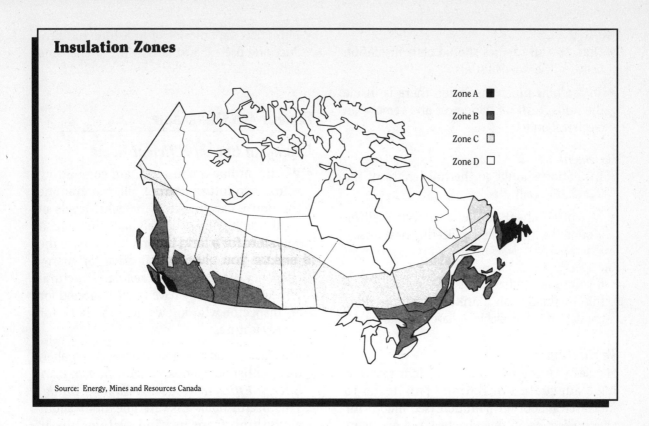

Zone A ■
Zone B ▨
Zone C ☐
Zone D ☐

Source: Energy, Mines and Resources Canada

Minimum Insulation

		Zone			
		A	**B**	**C**	**D**
Walls	RSI	3.0	3.6	4.1	4.5
Basement	RSI	2.2	2.2	2.2	2.2
Roof or ceiling	RSI	4.5	5.6	6.4	7.1
Floor (over unheated areas)	RSI	4.7	4.7	4.7	4.7

Source: Energy, Mines and Resources Canada

- Insulation should be at least 50 cm away from metal chimneys.

- Check for moisture damage; a leaking roof should be fixed before you consider adding more insulation.

- During winter, you can check your insulation from the outside. If there are bare patches on the roof where the snow has melted, it may indicate heat loss.

Walls

- Outside wall cavities should have insulation between the wooden studs.

- To see how much insulation there is inside the walls, turn off the power and remove an electrical outlet.

Basement

- Insulation should go the full length of the foundation wall.

- In winter, check to see if snow is melting around the foundation, indicating heat loss.

Garage

- If you have an attached garage, consider buying an insulation blanket or garage door insulation kit, available at hardware stores.

Ventilation

Houses that are particularly airtight may not have adequate ventilation. This leads to increased indoor air pollution (see Indoor Air Quality section in this chapter) and problems with excess humidity.

Some signs of inadequate ventilation are condensation on the inner surface of double-pane windows, and lingering odours.

Controlling Humidity

- If your furnace has an attached humidifier and your home has condensation problems, turn off the humidifier.

- Make sure that eavestroughs do not drain onto the walls of the house.

- Minimize the amount of moisture you produce and use exhaust fans in the kitchen and bathroom.

ENERGY AND OWNERSHIP

Buying an Energy-Efficient Home

- When you buy a house you are committing yourself to future heating bills, so examine the house carefully for air leaks, levels of insulation, tightness of seals and joints, etc. If you are making an offer for a house, have the house inspector do an evaluation for energy efficiency along with the regular structural inspection. You may have to shop around for an inspector who knows how to check for energy features.

- The Canada Mortgage and Housing Corporation has published a book called *Choosing An Energy-Efficient House: A Buyer's Guide*. This useful book answers questions about everything from heating systems to air vapour barriers, from insulation to ventilation, and provides a detailed checklist of what energy features to look for in a home. The book is available from the CMHC, 682 Montreal Road, Ottawa, Ontario K1A 0P7; (613) 748-2000.

- The National Research Council has published a free booklet, *Surveying an Older House: Inspection Checklist*, by C. S. Strelka. Order "Building Practice Note 47" from the NRC, Ottawa, Ontario K1A 0R6.

Building an Energy-Efficient Home

- The Canadian Home Builders' Association is actively promoting energy conservation through their R2000 project, which encourages builders to include energy-saving features in new homes. R2000 houses typically use from 60 to 80% less energy than conventional homes. For a list of builders in your area who build R2000 homes, contact the provincial office of the Canadian Home Builders' Association (see source list). The association also publishes a book called *Builder's Guide to Energy Efficiency in New Housing* and 17 booklets or "Builders' Notes" on energy conservation and safe building materials.

- The Canada Mortgage and Housing Corporation has produced many booklets on energy-efficient building techniques. Their *Energy-Efficient Housing Construction* is available from the CMHC in Ottawa.

- Contact your provincial ministries of energy and housing to ask if there are any grants or programs available to assist you in building an energy-efficient home. (Addresses in the blue pages of the phone book.)

- See the source list for addresses of organizations that can supply more information on building energy conservation right into your home.

Renovating For Energy Conservation

- Contact Energy, Mines and Resources Canada, your provincial ministries of energy and housing and the Energy Conservation Contractors Warranty Corporation (see source list for address) for free information on how to renovate for maximum energy conservation.

- Contact your provincial hydro company and ask if any grants or loans are available to assist homeowners in doing energy conservation renovations or retrofits. For example, B.C. Hydro offers a customer advisory service and publishes brochures on energy conservation topics.

- If you are thinking of planting trees around your home to provide shade in the summer, contact your provincial ministry of natural resources (see blue pages of your telephone book). They may be able to provide information about the kind of tree to choose and technical information about planting.

Energy Conservation for the Tenant

- Even if you don't pay for heating, you should turn down the thermostat at night or when you are out all day.

- If you don't have access to the thermostat and you find your apartment too hot, don't just open the windows: talk with your landlord.

- Consider doing some basic weatherstripping and caulking to conserve energy over the winter.

CONSERVATION TIPS

Water Heating and Water Saving

- One drop of water per second doesn't sound like much, but if you think of it as 16 hot baths a month or 2 swimming pools' worth of water every year, you might not find it so easy to put off that simple faucet repair job.

- Install a "water saver" or flow restrictor on your shower head to reduce water use by up to 50%. This device should be available at any department, hardware or plumbing store (or write to Great Northern Conservation Products Inc., Box 505, Markham, Ontario L3P 3R1).

- An "Econo-Flo" dam will reduce the amount of water used by your toilet. (Try a hardware store or write to Great Northern Conservation Products.) A bag filled with water and placed in the tank will also do the trick. (Some people use a brick, but small particles can break off and prevent the tank's outlet flapper from closing properly.) Alternatively, try bending the float ball rod so that the ball is lowered; this will reduce the water cut-off level in the tank.

- You can buy inexpensive aerators to add on to any faucet to reduce water consumption. Check your local hardware store.

- Insulating your hot water heater and pipes can reduce heat loss by up to 80%. However, if insulating a gas heater, do not cover the air intake or outtake vents. Call the gas company if you have any questions.

- Experiment with a lower temperature setting on your water heater. 60°C (140°F) is required by most dishwashing machines, but if you don't have a machine (or if you have a temperature booster on the dishwasher), try 54°C (130°F). (Turn off your main power switch before adjusting.)

- To check whether or not the toilet fittings are worn and causing unnecessary running of water, put a few drops of food colouring in the tank. If the coloured water seeps into the toilet bowl without flushing, then the fittings are leaking and should be replaced.

- You can also check to see if there are any water leaks by reading your water meter at night and again first thing in the morning.

- Avoid leaving the tap running unnecessarily. For example, instead of running the tap while brushing your teeth, wet your toothbrush and then fill up a cup for rinsing.

Preparing Your House for Winter

- Remove screens from all south-facing windows to get the benefit of passive solar heating (screens can block out as much as 20% of the sun's rays). However, on north-facing windows that do not get direct sun, the screens should stay on to provide extra insulation.

- Remove air conditioners and replace with glass and storm windows. If you don't take out the air conditioner, insulate on the outside.

- Prepare your furnace: contact a furnace maintenance company and ask them to clean filters; lubricate motor and fan bearings; and vent air from radiators.

- Look up your chimney using a mirror to make sure that there are no obstructions. You should be able to see the sky. If you can't, call a chimney cleaning or repair company for service.

- Put on storm windows and doors.

- Make sure that carpets, furniture and curtains are not covering heating vents.

- Check weatherstripping and caulking on doors and windows to make sure that they have not deteriorated.

Temperature: Staying Warm in Winter

- Setting your thermostat at 20°C will keep your house comfortable. (For every degree above 20°C, your heating bill could rise by approximately 3%.) However, at night or when the house is empty all day, there is no reason to keep the thermostat at 20°C. Most hardware stores carry automatic timers that can easily be installed on your thermostat; you can set the timer so that your household temperature is 17°C overnight and during the day. The timer can be set so that the house warms up early in the morning or before you return in the afternoon.

- Keep closet doors closed, so you don't heat wasted space.

- If your ceiling is over 2.5 m high, you may consider installing a ceiling fan to circulate hot air that rises.

- Aluminum foil behind all hot water radiators will reflect heat back into the room.

Vacation Tips for Energy Conservation

- If you are going away for more than five days, turn down your hot water heater.

- Use automatic timers for the few lights that you want to have on to discourage intruders, and switch to low wattage bulbs.

- Turn down the heat in winter to 10°C; turn off the air conditioner in summer.

- If possible, clean out the fridge and turn it off; leave the fridge door open when it is off.

- Unplug the television set if you have one with a remote control, "instant on." (Your set is using energy even if the picture is not on.)

There are a number of groups and publications that will provide more information on home energy conservation (see source list). In addition, governments and industry should be able to help.

- Energy, Mines and Resources Canada publishes a number of informative booklets on energy conservation. Their *Keeping the Heat In* is a particularly valuable resource. Energy, Mines and Resources also publishes a series of *Enerfacts*, pamphlets that provide specific information about draftproofing and insulation: how to determine what needs to be done, materials to use and the procedures involved. Contact the federal ministry at 580 Booth Street, Ottawa, Ontario K1A 0E4 or look in the blue pages of the phone book for a regional office and local number of Energy, Mines and Resources.

- Contact the provincial ministry of energy (see source list) for pamphlets on home energy conservation. Ask if there are any grants or programs to assist you in conserving energy. For example, Manitoba Energy and Mines has a Home CHEC-UP and CHEC Loan program in which an energy advisor will provide a free evaluation of your house. After the evaluation, you may be eligible for a loan to implement the energy advisor's recommendations.

- Contact your local hydro or gas company and ask if they have produced any pamphlets on energy conservation.

INDOOR AIR QUALITY

As energy-efficient homes become more and more airtight, we should be increasingly concerned over indoor air quality. As the air exchange provided by leaks, cracks and poor insulation decreases, so may the quality of air, if adequate steps are not taken to limit sources of indoor air pollution and to control ventilation in your home.

Some Sources of Indoor Air Pollution

Combustion Processes
- Furnaces and water heaters;
- Fireplaces;
- Gas stoves;
- Kerosene heaters;
- Auto exhaust from attached garages.

Building Products and Furnishings
- Synthetic materials, such as carpets, that give off gas or degrade over time and release small particles;
- Formaldehyde and other gases released from some building materials and products, such as particleboard and wood laminates;
- Fibrous glass in insulation;
- Asbestos in some building materials, particularly in houses built before 1976; for example, furnace ducts, heat shields, pipe insulation, acoustic ceiling tile, floor tile.

Appliances
- Improper venting of exhaust air;
- Humidifiers, air conditioners, dehumidifiers.

Human Activity
- Smoking;
- Chemical cleaners, waxes, polishes, air fresheners;
- Pesticides;
- Hobby supplies and paints.

Other
- Radon gas;
- Mildew and bacterial contamination.

For a number of air quality problems, it is possible to control pollution right at the source. You can, for example, limit the amount of synthetic materials in the home, stop smoking indoors, use non-chemical cleaners, use non-toxic paints and finishes, avoid aerosol products, and use biological pest controls.

However, indoor air pollution can also be controlled through proper maintenance of appliance and heating systems, and through adequate ventilation. All fuel-burning equipment requires a supply of fresh air for complete combustion and proper venting to the outside. If either of these conditions is not met, your furnace or water heater could be contaminating the air in your home with carbon monoxide and carbon dioxide.

Preventing Indoor Pollution

- Never obstruct the air openings, external vents, exhaust ducts, flues or chimneys of fuel-burning equipment such as a furnace, hot water heater, range, dryer or space heater. Check for blockage.

- Ensure that all vent hoods and pipes of fuel-burning equipment are in place and secure.

- If you have a new home with a fan-operated ventilation system, make sure it is in service and operating properly.

- Do not partition off your heating system in a confined space, unless you have allowed for an adequate supply of fresh air.

- Have a qualified service technician check your fuel-burning equipment once a year, preferably at the beginning of the heating season.

- Have your chimney checked and cleaned once a year by a qualified chimney contractor.

- Keep the number of synthetic chemicals in your home to a minimum. See Chapter 10, "Home: Getting Our Own Houses in Order," for a list of alternatives to chemical cleaners.

Plants for Fresh Air

Although by no means a cure-all, common house plants can be used to absorb some of the harmful gases found in most homes. Studies done by NASA indicate that the following plants actually reduce the amount of indoor air pollutants:

Spider plants: Remove formaldehyde, a common indoor pollutant found in particleboard, UFFI insulation, plastics, perma-press fabrics and carpets.

Philodendrons: Remove benzene and formaldehyde.

Detecting Air Quality Problems

- Backdrafting is the process by which harmful exhaust gases such as carbon monoxide, nitrogen dioxide and sulphur dioxide spill into the house rather than venting properly outdoors. It occurs when exhaust fans, fireplaces or even central vacuum systems alter the air pressure in your home, causing chimneys or vents to become air inlets. To determine whether or not your fuel-burning equipment is backdrafting, you can buy a simple detection device. Aptech Detectors Inc. has produced an "Air Check Combustion Backdraft Indicator," which they sell in packages of three strips. You place one strip on the furnace and one on the hot water heater. If the strip remains white, then your equipment is working properly. However, if the strip turns black, it means that exhaust spillage or backdrafting is occurring. Use the third strip to doublecheck — if it also turns black, you can be sure you have a backdrafting problem and should call a furnace or hot water heating repair service. Contact Aptech Detectors Inc., 547 Courtenay Avenue, Ottawa, Ontario K2A 3B4; (613) 729-4596.

- Also available is a sampling kit to test for the presence of contaminants in household air. Contact Bioquest International, Inc., 7 Loyola Bay, Winnipeg, Manitoba R3T 3J7; (204) 269-7264.

- Look in the yellow pages under Air Cleaning and Purifying for companies in your area that do air testing.

Radon

Radon is a colourless, odourless, tasteless radioactive gas that is produced when the natural radium in rocks and soils begins to decay. The gas travels through porous soil or is dissolved in groundwater.

As radon gas decays, it produces a radioactive particle known as a radon daughter. It is the radon daughter, rather than the radon gas itself, that poses a threat to human health. According to Health and Welfare Canada, approximately 5% of lung cancers in Canada may be caused by radon exposure (particularly in the uranium mining industry).

If radon enters a basement through earth floors, cracks and floor drains, it may accumulate in the home. Depending on the amount of radon, the level of ventilation and the degree of exposure, it may cause a significant health hazard to occupants.

Many factors affect the level of radon in any home: the amount of radon in the soil (which may vary greatly, even within one street), the level of air exchange in the home (which may vary from room to room), the construction of the house and the time of year (radon levels in homes are generally highest during the winter, when there is usually less ventilation).

The only way to determine whether or not radon is a problem in your home is to test for the presence of radon daughters and to determine the level of exposure.

The source list includes just a few of the companies in Canada that test for radon. Contact your provincial ministry responsible for radiation safety (see source list) for a complete list of companies in your area.

Health and Welfare Canada has established 20 picocuries per litre of air or 800 becquerels per cubic metre as a guideline for radon in the home, above which remedial action is recommended. (The U.S. guideline, however, is just 4 picocuries per litre.)

If your radon detection test shows results that are close to this action level, contact the provincial ministry responsible for radiation safety for information on remedial action.

Some radon problems can be reduced by blocking the gas's route of entry: for example, by plugging cracks and holes in basement floors and walls, installing a trap in floor drains, or covering sumps. Other methods may involve ensuring that adequate fresh air is entering your home, thereby flushing the gas out. Radon reduction can be a very difficult and technical job; it should be done by a trained specialist.

For more information about radon, contact The Canadian Institute for Radiation Safety, which has produced an information package on radon. The Canadian Home Builders' Association has produced a booklet, *Builder's Note #2: Radon*. (See source list for addresses.)

The U.S. Environmental Protection Agency has two free booklets on radon: *A Citizen's Guide to Radon: What It Is And What To Do About It* and *Radon Reduction Methods: A Homeowner's Guide*. Contact the E.P.A. at 614 H Street N.W., Room 1014, Washington, D.C. 20001; (202) 727-7728.

Green Consumer

> **Nobody made a greater mistake than he who did nothing because he could do only a little.**
> — Edmund Burke

The power of the consumer has often been exerted in boycotts, which suggest what we should *not* buy. Only recently has the flip side of this — the positive power of the purse in supporting environmental goals — made a real difference.

Take foam egg cartons, for example. One of the largest manufacturers in Canada decided to switch from ozone-depleting foam to cardboard because of consumer pressure. And this pressure did not take the form of an organized campaign; it came from average consumers asking in stores for alternatives to CFCs, average people voicing their concerns about global problems.

It may seem like an insignificant gesture to ask in your local stationery store for recycled paper products, but what if your request is just one in a long line of requests? It is almost impossible to know just what effect your questions, your concerns and your comments will have on a store manager or manufacturer, but you can be sure that you will have *no* effect whatsoever if you say nothing.

PURCHASING POWER

There are many ways to use your pocketbook to support environmental goals, many ways to vote with your dollars. Without a doubt, the process is not effortless: it takes work, it takes thought, it takes an inquisitive and informed consumer.

However, what is the choice? The first part of this book (along with daily newspapers, media reports, countless scientific studies, even government documents) shows that we cannot continue to consume without regard for the environmental effects of such consumption. We cannot continue to demand convenience above all else. Twenty percent of the world's population (in North America, Europe and Japan) cannot continue to consume 80% of the world's resources. Environment groups, the world's scientists, and the world's political leaders are all calling for change.

These are global issues, with resounding and massive implications for the future. But the question is, how do we, as individuals, go about translating these global issues into everyday action? One way to start is by looking at the environmental implications of our purchases.

Mike Nickerson, in his book *Bakavi: Change the World I Want to Stay On*, provides a useful series of questions that we should ask ourselves before buying any product:

• What materials are our purchases composed of?

• To what extent are these materials available?

• How much energy is needed to transport the raw materials, to produce the goods, to deliver them to retailers and to deliver them to us?

• Where do the resources involved come from, and how extensive are the reserves?

• What materials are used in production that do not appear in the product?

• What becomes of any by-products of production?

• Could the goods be made from other environmentally sound materials?

• What will become of the goods when we finish using them?

Obviously, these are complex questions and the answers will not be found in any one place (and certainly not on the product's label). Each one of these questions touches on complicated environmental issues: resource depletion, energy consumption, hazardous waste, toxic contamination, acid rain, global warming, ozone layer depletion, and the garbage crisis. And each of these questions invites us to take responsibility for our actions as consumers — to recognize that our habits of consumption are powering the machines that produce many of the world's most pressing environmental problems. The first step to taking responsibility as consumers is to ask the questions; the next step is to use the information about environmental problems to formulate answers.

BUYER BE AWARE

And if we don't buy widgets because we don't really need widgets, we'll save 100% of the energy [and resources and toxic by-products and landfill space] because another widget won't be manufactured to replace it.
Energy, Mines and Resources Canada, *The Garbage Book*

Canadian consumers have confirmed in numerous polls that, given the chance, they are willing to buy products that do not harm the environment even if they cost more. Given this overwhelming consensus, the question is now, how do we identify these products?

• "Environmentally friendly" products may be labelled as such. For example, the federal government has started a program called Environmental Choice, in which products that meet certain environmental criteria are identified with a logo.

Logo for "Environmental Choice" Products

Each dove represents a sector of society: consumer, industry and government. The doves intertwine, symbolizing that these sectors must work together to improve the quality of Canada's environment.

Source: Environment Canada

President's Choice GREEN products, based on the principle that individual consumers can make a difference. Their *GREEN* products include 100% phosphate-free detergent, toilet paper made from recycled paper, non-chlorine bleached, reusable coffee filters and biodegradable disposable diapers. Although questions have been raised about the integrity of an environmental program that includes disposable diapers at all, there is no doubt that the *President's Choice GREEN* line does offer consumers some valuable alternatives.

• Unfortunately, very few products are labelled according to their environmental impact. As a result, it is up to each of us to consume with care. This means, above all, educating ourselves about the issues. For example, once we know that many cleaning products create hazardous waste problems, we can choose alternatives, either by buying environmentally benign products or by making our own non-toxic cleaners. The key is to recognize an environmental problem (e.g., the garbage crisis), to understand what products contribute to the problem (e.g., overpackaged goods), and then to choose alternatives (e.g., buying in bulk).

All of the chapters in Part 1 will help you to recognize what products contribute, in general, to environmental problems, and will suggest alternatives.

For specific product information, see the sources listed for this chapter at the end of the book.

The first products recognized by the program in the summer of 1989 were re-refined motor oil, insulation made from recycled paper and selected products made from recycled plastic.

In another environmental initiative, the Loblaws food chain introduced a line of

From Consumer to Conserver

Without a conserver society, we could find ourselves with a resource-based economy and no resources.
— Lawrence Solomon, *The Conserver Solution*

"Enough" is an idea that we don't have enough of in our society.
— Mike Nickerson, *Guideposts for a Sustainable Future*

The basis of a conserver solution to global problems is simplicity itself: Don't waste. Only when this idea permeates all of our activities as a *goal* will the systemic flaws that allow for environmental degradation be worn down. This solution works at every level: don't waste at the manufacturing level (recycle materials, for example) and don't waste at the consumer level (buy products that last, for example).

How can we integrate conserver principles into our consumer habits? In the environmental education kit *Guideposts for a Sustainable Future*, Mike Nickerson sets out a series of guidelines or tools that people can use to evaluate whether or not any action is "sustainable"; and these guideposts can be used to examine our consumer habits in the context of conserver goals. For example, activities are non-sustainable (i.e., wasteful) when they:

- "require continual inputs of non-renewable resources": for example, leaving a store door open in the middle of winter to attract customers to the warm interior, or using open refrigerators in grocery stores;

- "use renewable resources faster than their rate of renewal": for example, felling trees without replanting;

- "cause cumulative degradation of the environment": for example, the manufacturing processes used to create most consumer products and most of the disposal techniques used to deal with the wastes of consumer products;

- "require resources in quantities that could never be available for all people": for example, goods for 20% of the world's population that consume 80% of the world's resources;

- "lead to the extinction of other life forms": for example, killing the Asian elephant for its ivory.

Activities are sustainable (i.e., compatible with the goals of a conserver society) when they:

- "use materials in continuing cycles": for example, when glass is recycled over and over;

- "use continuously reliable sources of energy": for example, solar power;

- "come mainly from the potentials of being human": for example, from communication, creativity, etc.

(For more information on these "Guideposts for a Sustainable Future" or to order an education kit, write to Guideposts for a Sustainable Future, P.O. Box 374, Merrickville, Ontario

K0G 1N0. Donations to support the educational work of the Guideposts Project can be made out to the Harmony Foundation Re: Guideposts Project and sent to 19 Oakvale Avenue, Ottawa, Ontario K1Y 3S3.)

These are general guidelines and there is no one source that will show us how to evaluate every activity or every consumer purchase. It is up to each one of us to look at our habits, inquisitively and thoroughly, and to take responsibility for our choices. And remember, the choice is essentially this: on the one hand we have more acid rain, global warming, ozone depletion, toxic contamination of the water, soil and air, deforestation, garbage production and wilderness destruction; on the other, a conserver society. The choice is clear.

15

Transportation:
The Fast Lane to What?

WORLD'S GONE MAD FOR CARS
— *Toronto Star*, May 20, 1989

For decades North Americans have been obsessed with the automobile. Like no other machine, the car has had an impact on almost all aspects of our economy, culture and social fabric. And as we navigate our way into the twenty-first century, we may find a world hotter and dirtier — radically transformed, in part, by this four-wheeled symbol of freedom and progress.

THE ROAD TO DISASTER

Motor vehicles are the single largest man-made source of hydrocarbon, carbon monoxide, and oxides of nitrogen pollution in Canada.
— *Motor Vehicle Safety Act*, Regulatory Statement

There are over 500 million vehicles (cars, trucks, ambulances, buses, etc.) on this planet — approximately one for every 10 people on earth. As with most other commodities, the vehicles are not evenly distributed among the world's population: nearly 40% are found, not surprisingly, in North America; 30% in Europe; 10% in Japan; the remaining 20% distributed among the rest of the world's inhabitants (80% of whom do not live in North America, Europe or Japan).

In 1986, there was one vehicle for every 1.7 residents of Canada; the United States had a closer ratio of people to vehicles — 1.4. China, on the other hand, had a ratio of 1 vehicle to 292 residents.

Every day, millions of cars in Canada pump carbon monoxide, carbon dioxide, nitrogen oxides and hydrocarbons and lead into the air, making vehicles the largest single source of some types of air pollution in this country. Of all the air pollution caused by human activity, automobile emissions account for 20% of nitrogen oxides, 15% of carbon dioxide and 24% of hydrocarbon emissions. The negative effects of these pollutants on the environment are widespread and well documented.

Nitrogen oxides and hydrocarbons react in the atmosphere to produce ozone (a major component of smog), which damages plants and causes respiratory damage in humans and animals. Oxides of nitrogen emissions lead to the formation of acid rain and other forms of acidic deposition. Carbon dioxide traps heat in the lower atmosphere and is the major cause of the greenhouse effect and global warming.

CUTTING DOWN

If you are really serious about clean air, then alternate forms of transportation will have to be used.
— Michael Renner, Worldwatch Institute, *Globe and Mail*, August 5, 1989

By asking yourself a few simple questions *before* you pick up the keys to the car, you could significantly reduce your use of this environmentally costly form of transportation.

• Am I using the car for convenience or out of a genuine need for this particular mode of transport?

• Will public transit take me where I want to go?

• Can I walk or use a bicycle instead?

• Can I combine this trip with other errands, thereby reducing the number of car trips I need to make?

• Can I double-up with someone else making a similar trip, thereby using one car instead of two?

If you need motivation to cut down on car use, remind yourself of the environmental savings of your personal reduction. For every kilometre that you *don't* drive,

• you are not contributing to acid rain damage;

• you are not contributing to the build-up of smog;

• you are not depleting fossil fuel resources;

• you are not contributing to the build-up of lead in the environment.

And if you find yourself asking how one kilometre can really make a difference, think of the other 11 million cars on Canadian roads: everyone's one-kilometre trip of convenience adds up to 11 million kilometres. At an average fuel consumption of 8.6 litres per 100 kilometres, that's thousands of litres of fuel wasted in approximately five minutes of mass convenience.

To monitor your vehicle use (and to avoid falling into the one-kilometre-makes-no-difference trap), it may be useful to keep a car logbook. On a sheet of paper, record the date, number of kilometres travelled (i.e., the odometer reading at the beginning and end of the trip), the purpose of the trip, the number of passengers in the car, the time it took, the cost of the trip (if you know approximately how much it costs you to run your car) and the parking cost. The next time you need to make a similar trip, try public transit, walking or bicycling. Compare the costs and the time involved. This is just one way to become more aware of your driving habits and to see how the kilometres add up.

If you find that you and other family members are using the car for many short trips, you may want to establish some ground rules. David Suzuki, in his radio series "It's a Matter of Survival," mentioned that his family uses the rule of thumb that if the distance is less than 10 blocks they walk or use a bicycle.

MAINTENANCE FOR FUEL EFFICIENCY

Studies have shown that over 50 percent of all cars on the road have deficiencies of one kind or another that cause excess fuel consumption and emissions.
— Environment Canada, *Air Pollution and Your Car*

According to the Rocky Mountain Institute, an environment and energy think-tank in Colorado, if every car and light truck in the United States improved gas consumption by just one mile per gallon, the same amount of oil would be saved as was imported from the Persian Gulf in 1985. And this massive saving alone could be achieved without any changes whatsoever to the way that cars are manufactured; it could be achieved simply by following a few basic maintenance rules.

Servicing
- Take your car in for a tune-up at least twice a year, preferably before the winter driving season and again before summer.

- If you notice any irregularities (such as repeated stalling or difficulty in starting), have a mechanic look for possible causes.

- Keep a log of your gas consumption; if you notice any increases that can't be attributed to changes in driving patterns (for example, increased city and less highway driving), the change may signal a problem.

- Not only will preventive maintenance help ensure that your car lasts longer; it will also save you money at the gas pumps. A proper tuning can increase fuel economy by as much as 15%.

Car Washing Tips
- Use a pail full of water instead of a hose, in order to save water.
- Use cold water and save energy.
- Use a phosphate-free detergent.

Tires

- For maximum fuel efficiency, radial tires are best. Although top quality radials may cost 2 to 3 times more initially, they last 4 to 5 times longer, in general, than regular tires and can increase fuel efficiency by 5 to 10%.

- When buying new tires, ask about energy-saving radial tires that can be inflated more than conventional radial tires, leading to lower fuel consumption.

- Tires should always be inflated to the maximum pressure designated by the manufacturer. This information can be found either on the tire sidewall, on a label in the glove compartment or inside the driver's door, or in the owner's manual.

- Check your tire pressure (when the tires are cool) at least twice a month and before any long trip. The pressure gauges found at most service or automotive centres will give a more accurate reading than most air pumps.

- Signs of wear on your tires' shoulders (i.e., at the "edges" of the flat part), may indicate repeated underinflation.

- When having your car serviced, ask the mechanic to check the wheel alignment. You can tell that your wheels are out of alignment if, on a straight and even stretch of road, your car seems to pull over to one side when you loosen your grip on the wheel. Another sign of misalignment is a tire that is worn down more on one side than the other.

- Although underinflation reduces the lifespan of a tire and increases fuel consumption, Energy, Mines and Resources Canada estimates that the average Canadian driver checks tire pressure only twice in three years instead of twice a month. A Transport Canada survey found that 60% of all passenger vehicles in Canada have seriously underinflated tires.

- Properly inflated tires can increase fuel economy by as much as 5%.

Proper Fuelling

- Leaded gas will be outlawed in Canada as of December 1, 1990, except for use in a very few commercial, farm and marine engines that require lead (and the amount of lead in gas for these exceptions will be reduced by 90%).

- Most cars on the road in Canada were designed and manufactured to run on unleaded gasoline. Misfuelling occurs when leaded gas is used in these vehicles. Now that the price differential between leaded and unleaded gas has been eliminated (the federal government removed a tax benefit that favoured leaded gas in 1987), there is no short-term saving in using leaded gas. In fact, misfuelling can *cost* you money in the long term.

- Leaded gasoline hinders the performance of cars designed for unleaded gas. According to *The Citizen's Guide to Lead*, misfuelling can result in increased maintenance costs of approximately $400 for every 80,000 km.

- Virtually all cars built after 1972 can use unleaded gas. In fact, some may benefit from using unleaded gas even if they were built for leaded. If your car is a pre-1972 model, ask your mechanic whether or not you can use unleaded gas.

- Misfuelling with leaded gas just 10 times can deactivate and, eventually, plug the catalytic converter, reducing engine performance, increasing fuel consumption and increasing the pollutants emitted by 5 times. In some provinces operating your vehicle with a malfunctioning catalytic converter (whether the result of misfuelling, deliberate tampering or faulty repairs) is, in fact, illegal. If you are having work done on your exhaust system, make sure that the mechanic has not deactivated the catalytic converter.

Oil

- A car runs more efficiently if the oil is changed regularly. Check your owner's manual for the manufacturer's recommendations.

- Approximately 425 million litres of used motor oil are discarded in Canada every year, yet only 25% of this oil is re-refined and reused. The 300 million litres that are dumped or buried represent not only a waste of non-renewable resources, but environmental contamination as well. If you change your motor oil, do not throw the old oil down the sewer; used motor oil contains toxins such as lead, cadmium and polycyclic aromatic hydrocarbons (PAHs) that contaminate

waterways. Instead, contact your provincial ministry of the environment or the provincial recycling council and ask for the address of the nearest gas station that will accept used oil for re-refining. If there is no station in your area, save the motor oil in a sealed and labelled container for the next hazardous waste collection day.

- If possible, buy re-refined motor oil for your oil changes. Much less energy is used in the re-refining process than is needed to refine crude oil. Loblaws produces re-refined motor oil under their *GREEN* label.

Battery
- Before replacing a weak battery, try cleaning the terminals with a pencil eraser (or ask your mechanic to do so). This allows the current to flow more freely by removing the oxides that have built up.

- When replacing a battery, do not throw out the old one. Either give it to a garage for recycling or save it for a hazardous waste collection day.

DRIVING FOR FUEL EFFICIENCY

If your car is maintained properly, there is still plenty of opportunity to save fuel by adhering to the following driving practices. Together they can lead to an increase of 15% in fuel efficiency (or 7.5 litres of gas saved per 50-litre tankful).

Driving Speed

- In general, cars run most efficiently at a steady 60-70 km/h. With increases in speed, gas consumption also rises; for example, fuel use increases by approximately 1% for every 1 km/h increase in speed over 100 km/h.

- Jerky starts and stops, along with sudden bursts of acceleration, all waste fuel. If possible, try to anticipate changes in traffic flow and accelerate or decelerate gradually.

- The Ontario Ministry of the Environment recommends that you place an imaginary glass of water or an egg on your dashboard and then drive in such a way that it will *stay* on your dashboard.

Braking

- It takes up to 6 times more gas to move a car from a complete stop than from even a few kilometres per hour. Try to reduce braking by slowing down as you approach stop lights. You may be able to avoid coming to a full stop before the light changes to green.

- If you are stopped for more than 10 seconds at a railroad crossing or while waiting for passengers turn off your engine (but *not* in traffic).

Gear Ratio in Standard Transmissions

- In general, cars consume more gas in low gears; therefore, it is better to change gears early and build up speed in higher gears.

Wind Resistance

- At highway speeds, up to 2% of your fuel is wasted because of increased wind resistance (or aerodynamic drag) from open windows. If possible, use the vents rather than windows for air circulation.

- Even an empty roofrack (especially the box kind) can increase fuel consumption from 5 to 20%. If you don't use the roof rack regularly, consider having it removed.

Weight

- Remove any unnecessary weight from your car. Every 45 kg of extra weight increases fuel consumption by 1 to 2%.

- In the spring, check the trunk and remove any winter driving supplies such as sand, salt, snow shovel, or traction treads.

Air Conditioner

- Before buying a car with an air conditioner, consider the other options for keeping your car cool in the summer months: buying a light-coloured car with cloth interiors, rather than vinyl, and tinted glass; or using removable shades when the car is parked.

- A car air conditioner can increase fuel consumption by 8 to 12% in highway driving and over 25% in stop-and-go traffic.

- Keep your car air conditioner maintained properly to prevent leaks of the ozone-depleting gases. Make routine inspections of the hoses, lines and fittings and look for signs of leakage or wear. Have your mechanic replace worn parts before they break down.

- Almost half of the ozone-depleting emissions from air conditioners occur during servicing. Try to find a garage that will drain and recycle the CFCs, rather than venting them into the air.

WINTER DRIVING TIPS

- In cold weather, hydrocarbon and carbon monoxide emissions from your car can double. Moreover, idling in cold weather increases pollution. However, a block heater with an electric timer can lead to a 10% fuel saving and reduced exhaust emissions. If the outside temperature is -20°C, the engine will need approximately 2 to 3 hours of block heating.

- Even in very cold weather (-18°C), most cars need only 15 to 30 seconds of idling before driving. The engine and drive-train warm up more efficiently when the car is being driven. If your car requires more idling time, it may be in need of servicing.

- Most cars function more efficiently in winter with low viscosity oils, such as 5W-30 or 0W-30. Check your owner's manual or ask your mechanic during the pre-winter service about the use of low viscosity oil.

- After a heavy snowfall, remove all snow from your car. Wet snow adds weight and increases gas consumption.

- Use the rear-window defroster only as long as needed to clear off the windshield.

- Remove snow tires in the spring. They increase fuel consumption.

Clean Driving Checklist

- Avoid taking short, unnecessary trips.

- Share the ride.

- Plan ahead to avoid heavy traffic and combine trips, if possible.

- Have your car serviced as least twice a year; make sure that your spark plugs are clean and firing properly and that your idle mixture is properly adjusted.

- Avoid jack-rabbit starts and jerky stops; try to maintain a steady speed whenever possible.

- Remember that excessive idling equals *zero* kilometres per litre and excess pollution.

- When filling up with gas, be careful not to overfill the tank — the excess may evaporate or be lost through the overflow pipe.

- Don't rev the engine before turning it off, you may contaminate the engine oil with gas and cause excessive wear on the cylinder wall.

- If you have a four-wheel drive system, disengage the four-wheel option when extra traction is not needed.

BUYING A NEW CAR

- Before buying a car, consider what you will be using it for and ask yourself if alternatives — such as public transportation or even taxis — would not meet your needs.

- The purchase of a car, like the purchase of any other energy-consuming product, means a commitment to fuel costs over the life of the machine. Every new car sold in Canada has been rated by the manufacturer in terms of its estimated fuel consumption. When shopping around for a new car, compare the fuel-efficiency ratings of different makes and models. The car dealership should have this information; if it doesn't, order the *Fuel Consumption Guide* from Transport Canada, Public Affairs Branch, 580 Booth Street, Ottawa, Ontario K1A 0E4.

- In general, the smaller the car's engine and the smaller the axle ratio, the lower the gas consumption.

- Automatic transmission, as opposed to standard or manual transmission, reduces fuel economy by up to 15%.

- An overdrive gear decreases fuel consumption during highway driving.

- Computerized or electronically controlled fuel injection systems, which meter the exact amount of fuel an engine needs for combustion, provide more efficient fuel consumption.

- Accessories such as power windows, air conditioning or a power sunroof all use energy when being operated and add to the weight of the car. Buy only those options that are necessary.

TRANSPORTATION ACTIVISM

If, as individuals, we are willing to reduce our use of automobiles, then alternative modes of transportation have to be available to us. Bicycles and walking are options that can easily

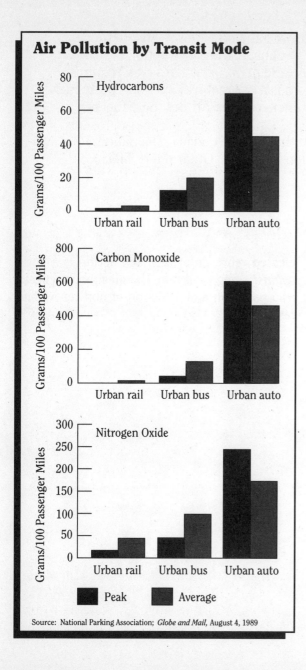

Air Pollution by Transit Mode

Hydrocarbons

Grams/100 Passenger Miles

Urban rail   Urban bus   Urban auto

Carbon Monoxide

Grams/100 Passenger Miles

Urban rail   Urban bus   Urban auto

Nitrogen Oxide

Grams/100 Passenger Miles

Urban rail   Urban bus   Urban auto

■ Peak   ■ Average

Source: National Parking Association; *Globe and Mail,* August 4, 1989

be used for short distances. However, for public transit and rail service, we depend on municipal, provincial and federal governments.

Because public transit requires large government subsidies, these systems have to be supported by the public before the service will be improved. However, an unfortunate circular situation has evolved. More people don't use public transit because in some cases the service is not convenient (e.g., buses are infrequent, trains are crowded); yet politicians won't allocate money to improve the service because it is not used enough. One way to break this cycle is for individuals to let their elected representatives, at both the local and the national level, know of their support for transportation initiatives.

Here are just a few suggestions of ways to encourage and improve transportation policies:

- Improve public transit.
- Provide incentives for high-occupancy vehicles (for example, lanes reserved for cars with 3 or more occupants).
- Improve bicycle lanes and paths.
- Improve traffic management techniques (for example, synchronize traffic signals for better traffic flow and reduced idling, or introduce one-way street systems for better traffic flow).

According to Transport 2000, a group that is working on issues related to the quality and availability of public transportation in Canada, the construction of new highways requires approximately 20 acres of land per mile, whereas rail requires just one-third the amount. A fully loaded compact car requires 3.5 times more fuel (per 1,000 miles) than a modern train; a jetliner requires 7 times more fuel per passenger.

Transport 2000 has seven regional offices throughout Canada. The national office may be reached at P.O. Box 858, Station B, Ottawa, Ontario K1P 5P9; (613) 594-3290.

It is possible (and in some communities encouraged) for individuals to get involved in these issues at a local level. At the very least, write a letter or make a phone call to your elected representative. Each action is a vote *against* smog, acid rain, the greenhouse effect, lead pollution and depletion of non-renewable resources.

16 Yard and Garden: Greening Your Own Backyard

One of the most obvious examples of our society's compulsion to master natural processes can be found in the parks, lawns and gardens of North America. For most of the growing season, we use up a great deal of energy (in the form of fossil fuels), water and hazardous chemicals in an effort to defy natural diversity. For some reason, we have come to believe that grass is the only thing that should be grown on lawns, and many people cling to this belief even if it means poisoning the soil, water, animals and air with chemicals in the process.

According to Friends of the Earth, pesticide use is 10 times higher, hectare for hectare, in Canadian cities than in agricultural communities — all in an effort to have conventionally "perfect" lawns. In addition, lawn maintenance requires huge amounts of water; in the summer months, water consumption triples as sprinklers and hoses are turned on. And if the grass clippings and yard wastes are not recycled as compost, this material ends up contributing to the garbage crisis.

Gasoline is another resource consumed by lawn-care: in the United States, lawn mowers use 200 million gallons of gasoline every year. Chemical fertilizers also require energy in the production process: it takes the amount of energy released by 5 tonnes of coal to make 1 tonne of nitrogen fertilizer, for example.

However, there are alternatives to energy- and chemical-intensive lawn and garden care.

NON-TOXIC LAWN CARE

A chemical gardener seeing a pest asks, "How can I kill it?"
An organic gardener seeing a pest asks, "Why is it there?"
— Judine Wilson, "Ten Ideas of How to Get Started in Organic Gardening"

It is possible to have a weed-free, disease-free and pest-free lawn without using chemical fertilizers, herbicides and pesticides. What it does take is vigilance (keeping an eye out for problems and dealing with them immediately) and an integrated approach (viewing any problems that arise as symptoms of unhealthy soil conditions or unhealthy plants, and using these signs to get at the cause of the problem).

The following lawn-care techniques will help you to prevent problems from occurring:

- **Mowing:** Grass should be mowed to a length of 7.5 cm (3 inches). This will keep the grass healthy and hardy (leaving enough of the blades to photosynthesize) and will allow the grass to crowd out weeds.

  After mowing, leave the grass clippings right on the lawn (as long as the clippings do not completely cover the grass). The clippings will provide a nutrient-rich mulch for the grass and discourage weeds.

- **Top Dressing:** If your lawn is looking patchy, sprinkle a thin layer of compost (see Chapter 11, "Garbage: Trim that Tonne," for more information on compost), top soil or composted manure over the lawn. (Do not use fresh manure, which will burn the grass.) The grass should not be covered; rather, it should be lightly dusted. You can then sprinkle grass seed over thin patches.

- **Hand Weeding:** If you watch for weeds and catch them early, before they spread, weeding will not be a huge task. It is important to pull out the root along with the weed.

- **Water:** Much of this precious resource is wasted by overwatering and by watering at the wrong time of day. The best time to water is in the early morning or evening (although

evening watering may encourage fungus and mould growth). The worst time to water is when the sun is strongest and when it is windy.

When watering with the hose or sprinkler, be sure to reach your target rather than the driveway or sidewalk. A sprinkler that does not throw water droplets high in the air is best. In general, an infrequent but thorough soaking is better than regular light watering.

Soil Testing

If you have a recurring problem in your lawn, it may be necessary to have the soil tested to determine if the problem is being caused by a nutrient deficiency. Phone your provincial ministry of agriculture (see source list for this chapter) to find out if it offers a free or inexpensive soil-testing service.

Reading Weeds

Weeds are excellent indicators of the condition of your lawn and soil. Before rushing to get rid of them, try to analyze what weeds are signalling about your lawn.

According to Stuart B. Hill and Jennifer Ramsay of the Ecological Agriculture Project in Quebec,

"The observant farmer and gardener will notice subtle changes in the weed populations on his land in response to his agricultural practices. As his soil improves, he may find that chickweed, chickory, common groundsel, and lambs-quarter become the dominant weeds. However,

if he finds that the daisy, wild carrot, mugwort, common mullein, wild parsnips, wild radish, and biennial wormwood become dominant, he should review his practices as these weeds thrive on soils of low fertility."
— *The Macdonald Journal*, June 1977

Hedge bindweed may indicate waterlogged or poorly drained soil; knapweed may reveal acid or low lime soil; and dandelions may indicate a clay or heavy soil.

The Cult of the Lawn

Why not clover instead of grass? An innocent-sounding question, but one that would send the chemical lawn-care business into a tailspin. (Manicured grass is big business: Canadians spent $50 million in 1988 on chemicals for their lawns and grass seed alone.)

The most important thing to remember is that there are alternatives — if your grass requires too much work and water, or if you have to *force* it to grow, or if you have to keep it weed-free with chemicals, there are other options that offer relief along with environmental benefits. Using a groundcover other than grass, or planting hardy native species are just two examples.

• **Groundcovers:** Groundcovers will grow in a wide variety of soils, climates and moisture conditions. They "hold" the soil, preventing erosion, and some groundcovers, such as clover, fix nitrogen from the air, thereby feeding the soil. (See the source list for books providing information on groundcovers.)

• **Native Species and Wildflowers:** Increasing numbers of gardeners are "going wild" in their own backyards. By establishing native plant populations, you will enjoy a more diverse yard that requires less maintenance, and you will also be providing habitat for indigenous birds, butterflies and wildlife. Establishing a native species garden does require a bit of research and imagination, but there are many gardening and environment groups that can offer assistance and a wide range of books that offer advice (see source list).

GARDEN

Many of the points covered under non-toxic lawn care apply to the garden as well. The most important feature of the garden is the soil and its nutrient content, composition and moisture level. The key to a healthy, organic garden is healthy soil.

Feeding the Soil

• In the spring, before planting, organic matter should be dug into the soil. Compost can also be used to "top dress" the soil during the growing season. In the fall, too, compost can be dug into the garden.

• Another way to feed the soil is to dig in composted manure. Fresh manure should be used only in the fall.

• Peat moss can be dug into the soil to improve its moisture-retaining capacity.

Organic Fertilizers

You can check the level of organic matter or nutrients in your soil either by having it analyzed or by examining it yourself. If the soil is sandy, or full of rocks, or clay-like in texture, then its organic matter content may be low. Dark, rich crumbly soils, which feel moist but not wet, are usually higher in organic matter. If the level is low, it may be necessary to apply organic fertilizers.

There are many reasons to choose organic fertilizers over synthetic ones. The manufacturing of synthetic nitrogen fertilizer requires a great deal of energy; synthetic fertilizers can adversely affect the soil by increasing the acidity; and if too much fertilizer is applied, the excess nutrients may contaminate water supplies.

Organic fertilizers are commercially available from garden centres and some grocery stores. Organic brands include (but are not limited to) *Canagro, Fossil Flower, Manchester Fertilizers, Safer's, Organeo* and *Purity Life*. If organic fertilizers are not available at your local garden centre, contact the companies shown in the source list for this chapter and ask for mail-order catalogues.

You can also make your own organic fertilizers, using materials that are readily available from garden centres. The following recipe is just one example:

Canadian Organic Grower's Organic Fertilizer

1 part bloodmeal
2 parts bonemeal
3 parts woodash or peat moss
4 parts leafmould or compost

For more details on the fertilizer needs of various plants under different conditions, see the books listed at the end of the book.

Coping With Pests, Organically

The best way to control pests, of course, is to prevent infestations from occurring. There are a number of ways to minimize the chances of pest infestation. The first is to keep the soil healthy and full of organic matter and nutrients — pests tend to attack weak plants.

You can also rotate plant beds from year to year. If a pest infestation has occurred in the previous year, you should be careful to clean up and destroy crop residues to minimize the risk of a recurrence.

It is also possible to adjust planting times to avoid pests' active breeding periods. For example, by planting carrots 3 weeks later than recommended (usually early May), you may reduce the chance of damage from the carrot rust fly.

Mulch

Mulch is anything that covers the soil — from newspapers, straw and grass clippings to wood chips and cocoa shells. (Some gardeners even use carpets, but it is best to use a natural or organic material that will eventually break down and improve soil texture.)

When mulch is placed around plants and between beds, it improves the moisture-retaining capabilities of the soil and stabilizes soil temperature. The overall effect is healthier plants and less chance of bug and weed infestation.

Planting Pest-Resistant Varieties of Plants

Some plants are more vulnerable to pest attacks than others. For example, green cabbage tends to have less resistance to the cabbage worm than does the red cabbage variety. Because plant resistance to pests may vary from year to year (and from seed company to seed company), try to find the most up-to-date information from your seed source. Some seed catalogues include this information, but you may have to phone the seed company.

Companion Planting

The benefits of some companion planting combinations have not been scientifically verified, but many gardeners swear by this method. Companion planting is a general term used to cover four different planting techniques: mixed planting, repellant planting, companion planting and trap planting.

Mixed planting involves planting several different plants in the same area, thus reducing the chance of pest infestation. Repellant planting is based on the idea that some plants actually repel insects. For example, parsley and onions planted near carrots may repel the carrot fly pest. The following plants are generally considered to be good repellants: marigolds, garlic, mint, cosmos, marjoram and oregano.

Companion planting involves placing certain plants in proximity to others because they grow better together. The combination of basil and tomato is one such example. Another form of companion planting is trap planting, in which certain plants are used as lures to attract pests. For example, dill planted beside tomatoes can be used as a trap for tomato hornworms; once on the dill, the worms can be handpicked and destroyed. (See the source list for books on companion planting.)

Controlling Pests

If you use the methods outlined above, you will reduce the need for pest control. However, when infestations do occur, there are many alternatives to chemical sprays. If the pests are not widespread, you may be able to handpick and kill them. For example, all you need is a flashlight and some gloves for a nightly hunt for slugs, cutworms or tomato hornworms.

Traps may also be used to rid the garden of pests. Some gardeners use a saucer of beer, for example, to attract slugs and earwigs. If you use mulches, they may also act as traps for bugs; lift up the mulch in the early morning and you may find slugs.

Beneficial insects or predators can be used to reduce pest populations. For example, ladybugs (or lady bird beetles) devour aphids. Bug-eating birds, toads, snakes, spiders, praying mantises, dragon flies and wasps are all beneficial to the garden. Insect parasites can also be used: for example, the braconoid wasp forms small white cocoons on the bodies of tomato hornworms, rendering them unable to reproduce. (For more information on where to buy beneficial insects, or for a list of books with more information, see the source list for this chapter.)

If these methods fail, you may decide to use a natural (rather than synthetic) insecticide or pesticide. There are many non-toxic sprays commercially available; for example, *Safer's* and *Fossil Flower* (check the label). Bacillus Thuringiensis (B.t.) is a commercial bacterium sold as *Dipel* or *Thuricide*. These products may be found at your local garden centre or ordered directly from the company (see source list).

You can also make a number of organic sprays that are effective at controlling pests:

Garlic Spray (attacks chewing and sucking insects and acts as a fungicide)

3 large cloves garlic, chopped
1 large onion, chopped
1 tablespoon pepper
1 litre water

Mix all ingredients in a blender. Strain through cheesecloth. Dilute 1:4 with water and place in a pump spray bottle. Apply to leaves and stems of plants.

Soap Spray (to control aphids, white flies, leafminers and spidermites)

Dissolve 2 tablespoons of soap or dishwashing liquid (such as *Ivory*) or finely-chopped soap in 1 litre of hot water. Mix and, when cool, apply to leaves and stems of plants using a pump spray bottle.

As a last resort, there are a few commercially available toxic botanical sprays. Although made from plants rather than synthetic chemicals, these sprays will kill beneficial insects along with pests; therefore, they should be used sparingly and only after trying other methods of control. *Rotenone* and *pyrethrum* are widely available. Both are toxic to fish and birds, and should not be allowed to contaminate waterways.

Identifying Pests
If you are not able to identify a pest and therefore unable to determine the best control method, contact the provincial ministry of agriculture to see if they offer pest identification services. (See the source list for the addresses.)

A Final Word on Pesticides
If you are determined to use a synthetic pesticide or herbicide (see Chapter 8, "Agriculture: Biting the Land that Feeds Us," for information about the harmful environmental effects of such use), there are a number of precautions to follow:

• Use the least toxic product available to treat the specific problem. Avoid products that promise "kill-all" solutions. The National Pesticide Information Service will be able to answer any questions about the relative toxicity of pesticides: 1-800-267-6315.

• Use only those products marked "Domestic" and not those marked "Agricultural," "Commercial," "Industrial" or "Restricted."

- Do not spray on a windy day. Wear a protective mask and gloves. Wash clothes in a separate load after use.

- Do not spray trees, flowers or shrubs when they are in bloom. In fact, in some provinces it is illegal to do so because of the harm pesticides do to pollinators such as bees.

- If you are spraying a plant that you will eventually eat, allow at least the minimum amount of time between spraying and eating that is listed on the label.

- If your spraying causes a drift of chemicals into a neighbour's yard and damages their plants, you may be legally liable for damages. Liability varies from province to province, depending on what is defined as an accidental chemical spill, and it is, of course, extremely difficult to prove that one person's spraying has caused damage in another person's garden. However, a general rule is to use chemicals in such a way that they do not contaminate a neighbour's property. (You may want to notify your neighbour *before* spraying; some people are sensitive or allergic to synthetic pesticides and may want to avoid being in the area at the time of spraying.)

- And finally, remember that bugs don't kill you, whereas pesticides may kill birds and poison other wildlife, contaminate groundwater and build up in humans.

End Note

This book includes many suggestions about what individuals can do to make a difference, and one of the themes running throughout has been the need to support environment groups.

There are over 1,800 environment groups in Canada, with hundreds of thousands of members, supporters and active workers. When we read in the opinion polls that 94% of the population is either very or somewhat concerned about the environment, we have these groups to thank. They are directly and indirectly shaping the future of the country — indeed, of the whole planet.

For the well-being of all populations — human, animal and plant — and for the health of all ecosystems — air, water and land — the people in these groups devote massive amounts of time, energy and money to the issues that affect each and every one of us. The work that environment groups do is fundamentally necessary if we are going to survive. But we can no longer sit back and let others do the work. We have created the problems and now we have to find and enact the solutions. Quite simply and quite clearly, the future is at stake.

If you can add any suggestions of what individuals can do to those collected in this book, or if you have any comments on the material herein, please write to Lorraine Johnson, c/o Penguin Books Canada Ltd., 2801 John Street, Markham, Ontario L3R 1B4.

Sources

Note on Sources

There are over 1,800 environment groups in Canada working on issues of vital importance. For information on groups active in your area or for groups working on specific issues, contact your provincial environment network (see below). A number of the environment networks publish resource directories and newsletters.

The listings of groups, books and magazines in the source sections for each chapter represent only a selection, suggestions of places to start looking for more information. Inevitably, you will find many more sources to add to the lists.

General

Provincial Environment Networks

Canadian Environmental Network
P.O. Box 1289, Station B
Ottawa, Ontario K1P 5R3
(613) 563-2078

Atlantic Environmental Network
3115 Veith Street
Halifax, Nova Scotia B3K 3G9
(902) 454-2139

Réseau québécoise des groupes écologiques
C.P. 1480, Succursale Place D'Armes
Montreal, Quebec H2Y 3K8
(514) 982-9444

Ontario Environment Network
P.O. Box 125, Station P
Toronto, Ontario M5T 2Z7
(416) 925-1322

Manitoba Eco-Network
P.O. Box 3125
Winnipeg, Manitoba R3C 4E6
(204) 956-1468

Saskatchewan Eco-Network
205—219 22nd Street East
Saskatoon, Saskatchewan S7K 0G4
(306) 665-1915

Alberta Environmental Network
10511 Saskatchewan Drive
Edmonton, Alberta T6E 4S1
(403) 433-9302

British Columbia Environmental Network
2150 Maple Street
Vancouver, British Columbia V6J 3T3
(604) 733-2400

Northern Environmental Network
P.O. Box 4163
Whitehorse, Yukon Y1A 3T3
(403) 668-5687

Environmental Law

Groups

Canadian Environmental Defence Fund
347 College Street
Suite 301
Toronto, Ontario M5T 2V8
(416) 323-9521

Canadian Environmental Law Association
517 College Street
Suite 401
Toronto, Ontario M6G 4A2
(416) 960-2284

Canadian Institute for Environmental Law and Policy
517 College Street
Suite 400
Toronto, Ontario M6G 4A2
(416) 923-3529

Environmental Law Centre
202, 10110—124 Street
Edmonton, Alberta T5N 1P6
(403) 482-4891

West Coast Environmental Law Association
1001—207 West Hastings
Vancouver, British Columbia V6B 1H7
(604) 684-7378

Books

Estrin, David, John Swaigen, and Mary Anne Carswell. *Environment on Trial: A Citizen's Guide to Ontario Environmental Law*. Don Mills: Canadian Environmental Law Research Foundation, 1978.

Howard, Ross. *Poisons in Public: Case Studies of Environmental Pollution in Canada*. Toronto: James Lorimer & Co., 1980.

Rovet, Ernest. *The Canadian Business Guide to Environmental Law: Protect Yourself! Protect Us All*. Toronto: Self-Counsel Press, 1988.

Sandborn, Calvin. *A Citizen's Guide to the British Columbia Environmental Appeal Board*. Vancouver: West Coast Environmental Law Research Foundation, 1988.

Swaigen, John, ed. *Environmental Rights in Canada*. Toronto: Butterworths, 1981.

Tingley, Donna, Patrick Kirby, and Raymond Hupfer. *Conservation Kit: A Legal Guide to Private Conservancy*. Edmonton: Environmental Law Centre, 1986.

Federal Government (Environment)

Environment Canada
Enquiries Centre
Ottawa, Ontario K1A 0H3
(613) 997-2800

Regional Offices of Environment Canada

Atlantic:
Environment Canada
45 Alderney Drive
Dartmouth, Nova Scotia B2Y 2N6
(902) 426-7231

Quebec:
Environment Canada
3 Buade Street
P.O. Box 6060
Quebec, Quebec G1R 4V7
(418) 648-7204

Ontario:
Environment Canada
25 St. Clair Avenue East
Toronto, Ontario M4T 1M2
(416) 973-1093

Western and Northern:
Environment Canada
2nd Floor, Twin Atria 2
4999—98 Avenue
Edmonton, Alberta T6B 2X3
(403) 468-8075

Pacific and Yukon:
Environment Canada
3rd Floor
Kapilano 100—South Park Royal
West Vancouver, British Columbia V7T 1A2
(604) 666-5900

Provincial Environment Ministries

Yukon:
Department of Renewable Resources
Box 2703
Whitehorse, Yukon Y1A 2C6
(403) 667-5460

Northwest Territories:
Department of Renewable Resources
Box 1320
Yellowknife, Northwest Territories X1A 2L9
(403) 873-7192

British Columbia:
Ministry of Environment
Parliament Buildings
Victoria, British Columbia V8V 1X5
(604) 387-1161

Alberta:
Department of the Environment
Oxbridge Place
9820—106th Street
Edmonton, Alberta T5K 2J6
(403) 427-2739

Saskatchewan:
Department of the Environment and Public Safety
3085 Albert Street
Regina, Saskatchewan S4S 0B1
(306) 787-6113

Manitoba:
Department of Environment and Workplace Safety and Health
156 Legislative Building
Winnipeg, Manitoba R3C 0V8
(204) 945-2587

Ontario:
Ministry of the Environment
135 St. Clair Avenue West
Toronto, Ontario M4V 1P5
(416) 323-4321

Quebec:
Ministère de l'Environnement
3900, rue Marly
Ste-Foy, Quebec G1X 4E4
(418) 643-6071

New Brunswick:
Department of Municipal Affairs and Environment
363 Argyle Street
Box 6000
Fredericton, New Brunswick E3B 5H1
(506) 453-3700

Nova Scotia:
Department of the Environment
5151 Terminal Road
5th Floor, Box 2107
Halifax, Nova Scotia B3J 3B7
(902) 424-5300

Prince Edward Island:
Department of Community and Cultural Affairs
Jones Building, Box 2000
11 Kent Street
Charlottetown, Prince Edward Island C1A 7N8
(902) 892-0311

Newfoundland:
Department of Environment and Lands
Confederation Building, West Block
Box 4750
St. John's, Newfoundland A1C 5T7
(709) 576-3394

Books

Allaby, Michael. *Green Facts*. London: Hamlyn, 1986.

Allen, Robert. *How to Save the World*. London: Kogan Page, 1980.

Berger, John J. *Restoring the Earth*. New York: Doubleday, 1987.

Bookchin, Murray. *The Modern Crisis*. Montreal: Black Rose, 1987.

Bookchin, Murray. *Toward an Ecological Society*. Montreal: Black Rose, 1980.

Brinkhurst, Ralph and Donald Chant. *This Good, Good Earth: Our Fight for Survival*. Toronto: Macmillan, 1971.

Brown, Lester, et al. *State of the World 1990*. New York: Norton, 1990.

Brown, Lester. *The Twenty Ninth Day*. New York: Norton, 1978.

Devall, Bill and George Sessions. *Deep Ecology: Living as if Nature Mattered*. Layton, Utah: Peregrine Smith, 1985.

Devall, Bill. *Simple in Means, Rich in Ends: Practicing Deep Ecology*. Layton, Utah: Peregrine Smith, 1988.

Dorfman, Robert, and Nancy Dorfman. *Economics of the Environment*. New York: Norton, 1977.

Eckholm, Erik. *Down to Earth: Environment and Human Needs*. New York: Norton, 1983.

Environment Canada. *Environmental Quality in the Atlantic Region 1985*. Dartmouth, Nova Scotia: Environmental Protection Service, 1986.

Environment Canada. *Human Activity and the Environment: A Statistical Compendium*. Ottawa: Statistics Canada, 1986.

Environment Canada. *State of the Environment Report for Canada*. Ottawa: Environment Canada, 1986.

Environment Canada. *What Atlantic Canadians Can Do For Their Environment*. Dartmouth, Nova Scotia: Supply and Services, 1989.

Environnement Québec. *L'Environnement au Québec*. Ste-Foy, Quebec: Environnement Québec, 1988.

Evernden, Neil. *Natural Alien: Environmentalism and World View*. Toronto: University of Toronto, 1985.

Goldsmith, E., and N. Hilyard, eds. *The Earth Report*. Camelford, England: Ecosystems, 1988.

Gorz, André. *Ecology as Politics*. Montreal: Black Rose, 1980.

Leiss, William, ed. *Ecology Versus Politics in Canada*. Toronto: University of Toronto Press, 1979.

Lovelock, James. *Gaia: A New Look at Life on Earth*. London: Oxford University Press, 1987.

———. *The Ages of Gaia: A Biography of Our Living Earth*. New York: Norton, 1988.

Myers, Norman. *Gaia: An Atlas of Planet Management*. Garden City, New Jersey: Anchor, 1984.

Ornstein, Robert, and Paul Ehrlich. *New World — New Mind: Moving Toward Conscious Evolution*. New York: Doubleday, 1989.

Our Common Future. Ottawa: Harmony Foundation, 1989.

Plant, Judith, ed. *Healing the Wounds: The Promise of Ecofeminism*. Philadelphia: New Society Publishers, 1989.

Seymour, John, and Herbert Girardet. *Blueprint for a Green Planet: Your Practical Guide to Restoring the World's Environment*. New York: Prentice-Hall, 1987.

Timberlake, Lloyd. *Only One Earth: Living for the Future*. London: Earthscan, 1987.

Ward, Barbara. *Progress for a Small Planet*. Harmondsworth, England: Penguin, 1979.

Ward, Barbara, and René Dubos. *Only One Earth*. New York: Norton, 1983.

World Commission on Environment and Development. *Our Common Future*. Oxford: Oxford University Press, 1987.

Magazines and Newsletters

Alternatives. Faculty of Environmental Studies, University of Waterloo, Waterloo, Ontario N2L 3G1. Quarterly.

The Ecologist. Worthyvale Manor Farm, Camelford, Cornwall, England PL32 9TT. Bi-monthly.

Environment. 4000 Albermarle Street N.W., Washington, D.C. 20016. 8 issues per year.

Environmental Action. 1525 New Hampshire Avenue N.W., Washington, D.C. 20036. Bi-monthly.

Environment Views. Alberta Environment, Main Floor, Oxbridge Place, 9820 — 106 Street, Edmonton, Alberta T5K 2J6. Quarterly.

Focus B.C. Sustainable Development Communications Project, 334 — 1367 West Broadway, Vancouver, British Columbia V6H 4A9. Monthly.

Greenpeace. Greenpeace, 578 Bloor Street West, 2nd Floor, Toronto, Ontario M6G 1K1. Bi-Monthly.

The Journal of Wild Culture: Ecology & Imagination. Society for Preservation of Wild Culture, 158 Crawford Street, Toronto, Ontario M6J 2V4. Quarterly.

The New Catalyst. Catalyst Education Society, P.O. Box 99, Lillooet, British Columbia V0K 1V0. Quarterly.

Probe Post. Pollution Probe Foundation, 12 Madison Avenue, Toronto, Ontario M5R 2S1. Quarterly.

State of the Environment Reporting. Environment Canada, Canadian Wildlife Service, Conservation and Protection, Ottawa, Ontario K1A 0H3.

Sustainable Development. Environment Canada, Canadian Wildlife Service, Ottawa, Ontario K1A 0H3. 3 issues per year.

The Trumpeter: Journal of Ecosophy. LightStar, P.O. Box 5853, Station B, Victoria, British Columbia V8R 6S8. Quarterly.

Women and Environments. 455 Spadina Avenue, Room 426, Toronto, Ontario M5S 2G8. Quarterly.

CHAPTER 1
ACID RAIN: AND SNOW, AND FOG, AND HAIL, AND . . .

Groups

L'Association québécoise de lutte contre les pluies acides
10763 Berri Street
Montreal, Quebec H3L 2H3
(514) 384-9867

Canadian Coalition on Acid Rain
(representing 56 organizations from across Canada)
112 St. Clair Avenue West
Suite 401
Toronto, Ontario M4V 2Y3
(416) 968-2135

Conservation Council of New Brunswick
180 St. John Street
Fredericton, New Brunswick E3B 4A9
(506) 458-8747

Ecology Action Centre
3115 Veith Street
Halifax, Nova Scotia B3K 3G9
(902) 454-7828

Prairie Acid Rain Coalition
Box 1288
Rocky Mountain House, Alberta T0M 1T0
(403) 845-3668

Society Promoting Environmental Conservation
2150 Maple Street
Vancouver, British Columbia V6J 3T3
(604) 736-7732

Government

The President
The White House
1600 Pennsylvania Avenue N.W.
Washington, D.C. 20500

Ambassador of the U.S.A.
100 Wellington Street
Ottawa, Ontario K1P 5T1

Books

Boyle, Robert H., and R. Alexander Boyle. *Acid Rain*. New York: Schocken, 1983.

Brown, Caroline, et al. *Rain of Death: Acid Rain in Western Canada*. Edmonton: NeWest, 1981.

Conservation Council of New Brunswick. *Acid Rain in the East: The Problem and The Polluters*. Fredericton, 1988.

Conservation Council of New Brunswick. *Rain Without Acid: The Atlantic Solution*. Fredericton, 1988.

Elsworth, Steve. *Acid Rain*. London: Pluto, 1984.

Howard, Ross, and Michael Perley. *Acid Rain: The North American Forecast*. Toronto: Anansi, 1980.

Luoma, Jon R. *Troubled Skies, Troubled Waters*. Markham: Penguin, 1985.

McCormack, John. *Acid Earth: The Global Threat of Acid Pollution*. London, England: Earthscan, 1985.

Park, Chris C. *Acid Rain: Rhetoric and Reality*. London, England: Methuen, 1987.

Pawlick, Thomas. *A Killing Rain: The Global Threat of Acid Precipitation*. Vancouver: Douglas and McIntyre: 1984.

Pollution Probe. *The Acid Rain Primer*. Toronto, 1988.

Regens, James L., and Robert W. Rycroft. *The Acid Rain Controversy*. Pittsburgh: University of Pittsburgh Press, 1988.

Schmandt, J., ed. *Acid Rain and Friendly Neighbors: The Policy Dispute Between Canada and the United States*. Durham: Duke University Press, 1989.

Weller, Phil, and the Waterloo Public Interest Research Group. *Acid Rain: The Silent Crisis*. Toronto: Between the Lines, 1980.

CHAPTER 2
THE GREENHOUSE EFFECT:
THE SKY'S THE LIMIT

Groups:

Alternate Energy Association of New Brunswick
P.O. Box 1434
Moncton, New Brunswick E1C 8T6
(506) 388-5922

Canadian Coalition for Nuclear Responsibility
P.O. Box 236 Snowdon
Montreal, Quebec H3X 3T4
(514) 489-2665

Cape Breton Alternate Energy Society
P.O. Box 1463
Sydney, Nova Scotia B1P 6R7
(902) 562-1404

Conservation Council of New Brunswick
180 St. John Street
Fredericton, New Brunswick E3B 4A9
(506) 458-8747

Ecology Action Centre
3115 Veith Street
Halifax, Nova Scotia B3K 3G9
(902) 454-7828

Energy Educators
229 College Street
Suite 206
Toronto, Ontario M5T 1R4
(416) 974-9412

Energy Probe
225 Brunswick Avenue
Toronto, Ontario M5S 2M6
(416) 978-7014

Friends of the Earth
251 Laurier Avenue West
Suite 701
Ottawa, Ontario K1P 5J6
(613) 230-3352

Pollution Probe
12 Madison Avenue
Toronto, Ontario M5R 2S1
(416) 926-1901

Trees for Today and Tomorrow
44 Eglinton Avenue West
Suite 206
Toronto, Ontario M4R 1A1
(416) 485-1907

The United Nations Association
2 College Street
Suite 116
Toronto, Ontario M5G 1K3
(416) 929-0990

Yukon Conservation Society
Box 4163
Whitehorse, Yukon Y1A 3T3
(403) 668-5678

World Federalists of Canada
145 Spruce Street
Suite 207
Ottawa, Ontario K1R 6P1
(613) 232-0647

Books

Bates, David V. *A Citizen's Guide to Air Pollution*. Montreal: McGill-Queen's University Press, 1972.

Dotto, Lydia. *Thinking the Unthinkable: Civilization and Rapid Climate Change*. Waterloo: Wilfrid Laurier University Press, 1988.

Garrod, S., M. Valiante, L. Ritts and M. Mellon. *The Regulation of Toxic and Oxidant Air Pollution in North America*. Don Mills: CCH Canadian, 1986.

Gribbin, John (ed.). *Climate Change*. New York: Cambridge University Press, 1978.

Schneider, Stephen. *Global Warming: Are We Entering the Greenhouse Century?* San Francisco: Sierra Club Books, 1989.

CHAPTER 3
LOSING THE OZONE LAYER: WHAT YOU CAN'T SEE CAN HURT YOU

Groups

Environmental Defense Fund
257 Park Avenue South
New York, New York 10010
(212) 505-2100

Friends of the Earth
251 Laurier Avenue West
Suite 701
Ottawa, Ontario K1P 5J6
(613) 230-3352

Worldwatch Institute
1776 Massachusetts Avenue N.W.
Washington, D.C. 20036
(202) 452-1999

Books

Dotto, Lydia, and Harold Schiff. *The Ozone War*. New York: Doubleday, 1978.

Gribbin, John. *The Hole in the Sky: Man's Threat to the Ozone Layer*. New York: Bantam, 1988.

Roan, Sharon. *Ozone Crisis: The 15 Year Evolution of a Sudden Global Emergency*. Toronto: John Wiley and Sons, 1989.

Magazines/Newsletters

Atmosphere. Friends of the Earth International. Available through membership with Friends of the Earth. Quarterly.

Chapter 4
Water:
Swimmable, Drinkable, Fishable?

Groups and Institutions

Atlantic Center for the Environment
Suite 1900
600 de la Gauchetière Street West
Montreal, Quebec H3B 4L8
(514) 843-8297

B.C. Watershed Protection Alliance
Box 9
Slocan Park, British Columbia V0G 2G0

Canada Centre for Inland Waters
867 Lakeshore Road
Burlington, Ontario L7R 4A6
(416) 336-4999

Canadian Ecology Advocates
15, rue Horatio Walker
Ste. Petronille, Quebec G0A 4C0

Conservation Council of New Brunswick
180 St. John Street
Fredericton, New Brunswick E3B 4A9
(506) 458-8747

Conservation Council of Ontario
489 College Street
Suite 506
Toronto, Ontario M6G 1A5
(416) 969-9637

Ecology Action Centre
3115 Veith Street
Halifax, Nova Scotia B3K 3G9
(902) 454-7828

Freshwater Institute
501 University Crescent
Winnipeg, Manitoba R3T 2N6
(204) 983-5000

Great Lakes Institute
University of Windsor
Windsor, Ontario N9B 3T4
(519) 253-4232

Great Lakes United
1300 Elmwood Avenue
Buffalo, New York 14222
(716) 886-0142

Greenpeace Canada
2623 West 4th Avenue
Vancouver, British Columbia V6K 1P8
(604) 736-0321

Greenpeace Montreal
2444 Notre Dame Ouest
Montreal, Quebec H3J 1N5
(514) 933-0021

Greenpeace Toronto
578 Bloor Street West
2nd Floor
Toronto, Ontario M6G 1K1
(416) 538-6470

International Joint Commission
Great Lakes Regional Office
100 Ouellette Avenue
8th Floor
Windsor, Ontario N9A 6T3
(519) 256-7821

Island Nature Trust
P.O. Box 265
Charlottetown, Prince Edward Island C1A 7K4
(902) 892-7513

Maritime Fishermen's Union
Pollution Committee
P.O. Box 1418
Shediac, New Brunswick E0A 3G0
(506) 532-2485

Northwest Atlantic Fisheries Centre
P.O. Box 5667
St. John's, Newfoundland A1C 5X1
(709) 737-4485

Ocean Resource Conservation Alliance
Box 1189
Sechelt, British Columbia V0N 3A0

Operation Clean Niagara
83 Gage Street
Niagara-on-the-Lake, Ontario L0S 1J0
(416) 468-3328

Petroleum Association for Conservation of the Canadian
Environment
1202—275 Slater Street
Ottawa, Ontario K1P 5H9
(613) 236-9122

Pollution Probe
12 Madison Avenue
Toronto, Ontario M5R 2S1
(416) 926-1907

Prairie Association for Water Management
Box 1949
Hanna, Alberta T0J 1P0
(403) 854-2509

Rivers Defense Coalition
Box 2781
Smithers, British Columbia V0J 2N0
(604) 847-9693

St. Lawrence Centre/Centre St. Laurent
(information centre on St. Lawrence ecosystem and marine park)
105 McGill Street
4th Floor
Montreal, Quebec H2Y 2E7
(514) 283-7000

Sea Shepherd Conservation Society
Box 48446
Vancouver, British Columbia V7X 1A2
(604) 688-7325

Société pour vaincre la pollution
C.P. 65
Place d'Armes
Montreal, Quebec H2Y 3E9
(514) 844-5477

Society Promoting Environmental Conservation
2150 Maple Street
Vancouver, British Columbia V6J 3T3
(604) 736-7732

Water Protection Group
14 Mount Royal Crescent
Winnipeg, Manitoba R3J 2M9

Books

Ashworth, William. *The Late, Great Lakes: An Environmental History*. New York: Knopf, 1986.

Conservation Council of New Brunswick. *The Groundwater Pollution Primer*, Fredericton, 1987.

Cooper, Kathy, and Kai Millyard. *The Great Lakes Primer*. Toronto: Pollution Probe, 1986.

Costner, Pat, and Holly Gettings. *We All Live Downstream: A Guide to Waste Treatment That Stops Water Pollution*. Eureka Springs, Arkansas: The Water Center, 1986.

Environment Canada and United States Environmental Protection Agency. *The Great Lakes: An Environmental Atlas and Resource Book*. Toronto: Environment Canada, 1987.

Foster, Harold D., and W.R. Derrick Sewell. *Water: The Emerging Crisis in Canada*. Toronto: James Lorimer & Co., 1981.

Hammond, Susan, and Herb Hammond. *B.C. Watershed Protection Alliance Handbook*. Available from Box 9, Slocan Park, B.C. V0G 2G0.

Holm, Wendy, ed., *Water and Free Trade*. Toronto: James Lorimer & Co. 1988.

Keating, Michael. *To the Last Drop: Canada and the World's Water Crisis*. Toronto: Macmillan, 1986.

Sanger, Clyde. *Ordering the Oceans*. Toronto: University of Toronto Press, 1987.

Magazines/Newsletters

Canadian Water Watch. The Rawson Academy of Aquatic Science, Suite 1025, 130 Slater Street, Ottawa, Ontario K1P 6E2. Monthly.

Water Pollution Research Journal of Canada. Waste Water Technology Centre, P.O. Box 5050, Burlington, Ontario L7R 4A6. Quarterly.

Chapter 5
Vanishing Forests:
Slash, Burn — and Gone

Groups

Calgary Rain Forest Action Group
100 Sandstone Road NW
Calgary, Alberta T3K 2N3
(403) 275-0247

Canadians for Conservation of Tropical Nature
Faculty of Environmental Studies
York University
4700 Keele Street
North York, Ontario M3J 1P3
(416) 736-5252

Friends of the Earth
251 Laurier Avenue West
Suite 701
Ottawa, Ontario K1P 5J6
(613) 230-3352

Friends of the Rainforest
Department of Biology
Carleton University
Ottawa, Ontario K1S 5B6
(613) 236-5751

International Wildlife Coalition
121 Richmond Street West
Suite 203
Toronto, Ontario M5H 2K1
(416) 368-4661

Pollution Probe
12 Madison Avenue
Toronto, Ontario M5R 2S1
(416) 926-1907

Probe International
225 Brunswick Avenue
Toronto, Ontario M5S 2M6
(416) 978-7014

Rainforest Action Group of Edmonton
10511 Saskatchewan Drive
Edmonton, Alberta T6E 4S1
(403) 433-8711

Rainforest Action Network
300 Broadway
Suite 28
San Francisco, California 94133
(415) 398-4404

Western Canada Wilderness Committee
20 Water Street
Vancouver, British Columbia V6B 1A4
(604) 683-8220

World Wildlife Fund
60 St. Clair Avenue East
Suite 201
Toronto, Ontario M4T 1N5
(416) 923-8173

Government Departments

Minister of Finance and Canadian Governor to the World Bank
House of Commons
Ottawa, Ontario K1A 0A6
(no postage necessary)

Secretary of State for External Affairs and Canadian Governor to
the Regional Multilateral Development Banks
House of Commons
Ottawa, Ontario K1A 0A6
(no postage necessary)

Minister for External Affairs and International Development
(responsible for CIDA)
House of Commons
Ottawa, Ontario K1A 0A6
(no postage necessary)

Books

Adams, Patricia, and Lawrence Solomon. *In the Name of Progress: The Underside of Foreign Aid*. Toronto: Doubleday, 1985.

Caufield, Catherine. *In the Rainforest*. New York: Knopf, 1985.

Forsyth, Adrian. *Tropical Nature*. New York: Scribner, 1984.

Gradwohl, Judith, and Russell Greenberg. *Saving the Rainforest*. London: Earthscan, 1988.

Hecht, Susanna, and Alexander Cockburn. *The Fate of the Forest: Developers, Destroyers and Defenders of the Amazon*. London: Verso, 1989.

Myers, Norman. *The Primary Source: Tropical Forests and Our Future*. New York: Norton, 1985.

Ehrhardt, Roger et al. *Canadian Aid and the Environment*. Ottawa: North South Institute, 1981.

Sting and Jean-Pierre Deutilleux. *The Fight for the Amazon*. New York: Little Brown & Company, 1989.

Magazines/Newsletters

Environesia. Indonesian Environmental Forum, WALHI, Jalan Penjernihan 1, Konplek Keuangan Number 15, Pejompongan, Jakarta Pusat 10210, Indonesia. Four issues a year.

Environmental News Digest. Friends of the Earth, Malaysia, SAM, 43 Salween Road, Penan 10050, Malaysia.

World Rainforest Report. Rainforest Action Network, San Francisco. Available from Probe International. Quarterly.

CHAPTER 6
GARBAGE:
OUR GROSS NATIONAL PRODUCT

Groups

Citizens Network on Waste Management
139 Waterloo Street
Kitchener, Ontario N2H 3V5
(519) 744-7503

The Clean Nova Scotia Foundation
P.O. Box 2528
Station M
Halifax, Nova Scotia B3J 3N5
(902) 424-5245

Outdoors Unlittered
45, 9912 — 106 Street
Edmonton, Alberta T5K 1C5
(403) 429-0517

Outdoors Unlittered
200-1676 Martin Drive
White Rock, British Columbia V4A 6E7
(604) 538-4085

Pollution Probe
12 Madison Avenue
Toronto, Ontario M5R 2S1
(416) 926-1907

Saskatchewan Environmental Society
205 — 219 22nd Street East
Saskatoon, Saskatchewan S7K 0G4
(306) 665-1915

Society Promoting Environmental Conservation
2150 Maple Street
Vancouver, British Columbia V6J 3T3
(604) 736-7732

Western Canada Wilderness Committee
20 Water Street
Vancouver, British Columbia V6B 1A4
(604) 683-8220

Provincial Recycling Groups

Recycling Council of British Columbia
2150 Maple Street
Vancouver, British Columbia V6J 3T3
(604) 731-7222

Recycling Council of Alberta
3415 Ogden Road SE
Calgary, Alberta T2G 4N4
(403) 262-4542

Saskatchewan Environmental Society
205— 219 22nd Street East
Saskatoon, Saskatchewan S7K 0G4
(306) 665-1915

Recycling Council of Manitoba
412 McDermott Avenue
Winnipeg, Manitoba R3A 0A9
(204) 942-7781

Recycling Council of Ontario
489 College Street
Suite 504
Toronto, Ontario M6G 1A5
(416) 960-0938
1-800-263-2849

Fonds québécois de récupération
407, boulevard St. Laurent
Suite 500
Montreal, Quebec H2Y 2V5
(514) 874-3701

Ecology Action Centre
3115 Veith Street
Halifax, Nova Scotia B3K 3G9
(902) 454-7828

Conservation Council of New Brunswick
180 St. John Street
Fredericton, New Brunswick E3B 4A9
(506) 458-8747

Recycled Paper

Earthcycle Paper Corp.
P.O. Box 3884
High River, Alberta T0L 1B0
(403) 652-2650

The Paper Choice
2659 Trinity Street
Vancouver, British Columbia V5K 1E5
(604) 253-4611

The Paper Source
Fallbrook, Ontario K0G 1A0
(613) 267-7191

The Paper Trail
779 3rd Street N.W.
Calgary, Alberta T2N 1P1
(403) 270-0271

Waste Exchanges

Alberta Waste Materials Exchange
Box 8330, Station F
Edmonton, Alberta T6H 5X2
(403) 450-5402

British Columbia Waste Exchange
2150 Maple Street
Vancouver, British Columbia V6J 3T3
(604) 731-7222

Canadian Waste Materials Exchange
2395 Speakman Drive
Sheridan Park
Mississauga, Ontario L5K 1B3
(416) 822-4111

Manitoba Waste Exchange
1329 Niakwa Road East
Winnipeg, Manitoba R2J 3T4
(204) 257-3891

Ontario Waste Exchange
2395 Speakman Drive
Sheridan Park
Mississauga, Ontario L5K 1B3
(416) 822-4111

Books

Campbell, Monica E., and William M. Glenn. *Profit from Pollution Prevention: A Guide to Industrial Waste Reduction and Recycling*. Toronto: Pollution Probe, 1982.

Crooks, Harold. *Dirty Business: The Inside Story of the New Garbage Agglomerates*. Toronto: James Lorimer & Co.,1983.

Hassol, Susan, and Beth Richman. *Recycling: 101 Practical Tips for Home and Work*. Snowmass, Colorado: Windstar Foundation, 1989.

Kidd, Joanna. *A Burning Question: Air Emissions from Municipal Refuse Incinerators*. Toronto: Pollution Probe, 1984.

Solomon, Lawrence. *The Conserver Solution*. Toronto: Doubleday, 1978.

The University Recycling Reader: A Guide to Setting Up a Fine Paper Recycling Program on Your Campus. B.C. Public Interest Research Group. TC 304, Simon Fraser University, Burnaby, British Columbia V5A 1S6; (604) 291-4360.

CHAPTER 7
HAZARDOUS WASTES AND TOXIC SUBSTANCES

Groups

Citizens Network on Waste Management
139 Waterloo Street
Kitchener, Ontario N2H 3V5
(519) 744-7503

Concerned Citizens of Manitoba
204 Arnold Avenue
Winnipeg, Manitoba R3L 0W5

Friends of the Earth
251 Laurier Avenue West
Suite 701
Ottawa, Ontario K1P 5J6
(613) 230-3352

Greenpeace Canada
2623 West 4th Avenue
Vancouver, British Columbia V6K 1P8
(604) 736-0321

Greenpeace Montreal
2444, Notre Dame Ouest
Montreal, Quebec H3J 1N5
(514) 933-0021

Greenpeace Toronto
578 Bloor Street West
2nd Floor
Toronto, Ontario M6G 1K1
(416) 538-6470

Ontario Toxic Waste Research Coalition
Box 35
Vineland Station, Ontario L0R 2E0
(416) 935-8833

Pollution Probe
12 Madison Avenue
Toronto, Ontario M5R 2S1
(416) 926-1907

Société pour vaincre la pollution
C.P. 65
Place d'Armes
Montreal, Quebec H2Y 3E9
(514) 844-5477

Society Promoting Environmental Conservation
2150 Maple Street
Vancouver, British Columbia V6J 3T3
(604) 736-7732

Toxics Watch Society of Alberta
10511 Saskatchewan Drive
Edmonton, Alberta T6E 4S1
(403) 433-8711

Institutions

Canadian Centre for Occupational Health and Safety
250 Main Street East
Hamilton, Ontario L8N 1H6
(416) 572-2981 or 1-800-263-8276

Canadian Centre for Toxicology
645 Gordon Street
Guelph, Ontario N1G 2W1
(519) 837-3320

Canadian Chemical Producers' Association
350 Sparks Street
Suite 805
Ottawa, Ontario K1R 7S8
(613) 237-6215

Canadian Institute for Radiation Safety
595 Bay Street
Suite 1050
Toronto, Ontario M5G 2C2
(416) 596-1617

Crown Agencies

Alberta Special Waste Management Corporation
9th Floor, Pacific Plaza
10909 Jasper Avenue
Edmonton, Alberta T5J 3L9
(403) 422-5029

Manitoba Hazardous Waste Management Corporation
226-530 Century Street
Winnipeg, Manitoba R3H 0Y4
(204) 945-1844 or 1-800-782-2474

Ontario Waste Management Corporation
2 Bloor Street West
11th Floor
Toronto, Ontario M4W 3E2
(416) 923-2918 or 1-800-268-1178

Books

Bertell, Rosalie. *No Immediate Danger? Prognosis for a Radioactive Earth*. Toronto: Women's Press, 1985.

Brodeur, Paul. *Outrageous Misconduct: The Asbestos Industry on Trial*. New York: Pantheon, 1985.

Brown, Michael H. *Laying Waste: The Poisoning of America by Toxic Chemicals*. New York: Pantheon, 1980.

———. *The Toxic Cloud: The Poisoning of America's Air*. New York: Harper and Row, 1988.

Caufield, Catherine. *Multiple Exposures: Chronicles of the Radiation Age*. Toronto: Stoddart, 1989.

Cooper, Kathy, and Barbara Wallace. *The Citizen's Guide to Lead*. Toronto: NC Press, 1986.

Crone, Hugh D. *Chemicals and Society: A Guide to the New Chemical Age*. New York: Cambridge University Press, 1986.

Howard, Ross. *Poisons in Public: Case Studies of Environmental Pollution in Canada*. Toronto: James Lorimer & Co., 1980.

Jackson, John, Phil Weller and the Waterloo Public Interest Research Group. *Chemical Nightmare: The Unnecessary Legacy of Toxic Wastes*. Toronto: Between the Lines, 1983.

Kruss, P., and I.M. Valeriote. *Controversial Chemicals: A Citizen's Guide*. Montreal: Multiscience Publications, 1979.

McCann, Michael. *Artist Beware*. New York: Watson-Guptill Publications, 1979.

Nader, Ralph, Ronald Brownstein and John Richard, eds. *Who's Poisoning America: Corporate Polluters and their Victims in the Chemical Age*. San Francisco: Sierra Club Books, 1981.

Proctor, N.H., J.P. Hughes and M.L. Fischman. *Chemical Hazards of the Workplace*. New York: Lippincott, 1988.

Reasons, C., L. Ross and C. Patterson. *Assault on the Worker: Occupational Health and Safety in Canada*. Toronto: Butterworths, 1981.

Sittig, Marshall. *Handbook of Toxic and Hazardous Chemicals*. Park Ridge, New Jersey: Noyes Publications, 1981.

Simon, Paul L. *Hazardous Products; Canada's Right-to-Know Laws*. Toronto: CCH, 1987.

Wright, Cameron, and the Waterloo Public Interest Research Group. *A Worker's Guide to Solvent Hazards*. Waterloo, Ontario: Waterloo Public Interest Research Group, 1988.

Magazines/Newsletters

Alive. Canadian Health Reform Products. Available from 4728 Byrne Road, Burnaby, British Columbia V5J 3H7, (604) 438-1919. 8 issues per year.

Leaking Underground Storage Tanks. Industrial Programs Branch, Environment Canada, Ottawa, Ontario K1A 0H3; (819) 953-1125. Quarterly.

Living Safety. Canadian Safety Council, 1765 St. Laurent Boulevard, Ottawa, Ontario K1G 3V4; (613) 521-6881. Quarterly.

CHAPTER 8
AGRICULTURE:
BITING THE LAND THAT FEEDS US

Groups

Agriculture Alternatives
Box 244
University Centre
University of Guelph
Guelph, Ontario N1G 2W1

B.C. Association for Regenerative Agriculture
P.O. Box 1601
Aldergrove, British Columbia V0X 1A0

B.C. Coalition for Alternatives to Pesticides
R.R. #1
Sechelt, British Columbia V0N 3A0
(604) 885-3618

B.C. Organic Growers
Box 11
Lytton, British Columbia V0K 1Z0

Food Irradiation Alert
Health Action Network Society
#202—5262 Rumble Street
Burnaby, British Columbia V5J 2B6
(604) 435-0512

Canadian Environmental Defence Fund
347 College Street
Suite 301
Toronto, Ontario M5T 2V8
(416) 323-9521

Canadian Organic Growers
P.O. Box 6408, Station J
Ottawa, Ontario K2A 3Y6
(613) 259-2967

Christian Farmers Federation of Alberta
10766-97 Street
Edmonton, Alberta T5H 2M1
(403) 421-8382

Christian Farmers Federation of Ontario
115 Woolwich Street
Guelph, Ontario N1H 3V1
(519) 837-1620

Earthcare
Box 1810, Station A
Kelowna, British Columbia V1Y 8P2
(604) 861-4788

Ecological Agriculture Projects
P.O. Box 191
Macdonald College
21, 111 Lakeshore Road
Ste-Anne de Bellevue, Quebec H9X 1C0
(514) 398-7771

Ecological Farmers Association of Ontario
R.R. #1
Tiverton, Ontario N0G 2T0
(519) 368-7417

Fédération des agriculteurs/trices francophones du Nouveau-Brunswick
165, boulevard Hébert
Edmundston, New Brunswick E3V 2S8
(506) 735-4886

Friends of Foodland
295 Water Street, Unit 25
Guelph, Ontario N1G 2X5
(519) 763-2589

Green Web
R. R. #3
Saltsprings,
Pictou County, Nova Scotia B0K 1P0

Maritime Sustainable Agriculture Network
R.R. #1
Wolfville, Nova Soctia B0P 1X0
(902) 678-1799

Mouvement pour l'agriculture biologique
4545, avenue Pierre-de-Coubertin
C.P. 1000, Succ. M
Montréal, Québec H1V 3R2
(514) 252-3039

Nova Scotia Coalition for Alternatives to Pesticides
Box 643
Baddeck, Nova Scotia B0E 1B0
(902) 295-3053

Organic Crop Improvement Association Ontario
Box 8000
Lindsay, Ontario K9V 5E6
(705) 324-2709

Organic Crop Improvement Association New Brunswick
R.R. #5
Debec, New Brunswick E0J 1J0
(506) 277-6371

Organic Crop Improvement Association Nova Scotia
Box 116
Walton, Nova Scotia B0N 2R0

Organic Crop Improvement Association Prince Edward Island
Dover, Prince Edward Island C0A 1W0
(902) 962-3527

Organic Crop Improvement Association Quebec
475, chemin Hyatt Mills
Compton, Quebec J0B 1L0
(819) 849-2270

Organic Crop Improvement Association Saskatchewan
Box 69
Davidson, Saskatchewan S0G 1A0
(306) 567-4260

Prairie Farm Rehabilitation Association
1901 Victoria Avenue
Regina, Saskatchewan S4P 0R5
(306) 780-5070

Preservation of Agricultural Lands Society
Box 1090
St. Catharines, Ontario L2R 7A3
(416) 684-3383

Protect Agricultural Land
R.R. #4
Lacombe, Alberta T0C 1S0
(403) 782-2517

Sustainable Agriculture Association of Alberta
Box 1063
Nanton, Alberta T0L 1R0
(403) 646-5752

Sustainable Agriculture Movement of Manitoba
492 Camden Place
Winnipeg, Manitoba R3G 2V7

Syndicat des agriculteurs biologiques du Québec
555, boulevard Rolland-Therrien
Longueil, Quebec J4H 3Y9
(514) 679-0530

Books

Altieri, Miguel A. *Agroecology: The Scientific Basis of Alternative Agriculture*. Berkeley: University of California Press, 1983.

Americans for Safe Food. *Guess What's Coming to Dinner: Contaminants in our Food*. Washington: Center for Science in the Public Interest, 1987. Available from Center for Science in the Public Interest, 1501 16th Street N.W., Washington, D.C. 20036.

Bennett, Jon. *The Hunger Machine: The Politics of Food*. Montreal: CBC Enterprises, 1987.

Carson, Rachel. *The Silent Spring*. Boston: Houghton Mifflin, 1962.

Christian Farmers Federation. *Pesticides: Something to Think About*. (See source list for address.)

Dover, Michael, and Lee Talbot. *To Feed the Earth: Agro-Ecology for Sustainable Development*. Washington, D.C.: World Resources Institute, 1987.

Dudley, Nigel. *This Poisoned Earth: The Truth About Pesticides*. London: Piatkus, 1987.

Fairbairn, G.L. *Will the Bounty End? The Uncertain Future of Canada's Food Supply*. Saskatoon: Western Producer Prairie Books, 1987.

Giangrande, Carol. *Down to Earth: The Crisis in Canadian Farming*. Toronto: Anansi, 1985.

Hall-Beyer, Bart, and Jean Richard. *Ecological Fruit Production in the North*. Scotstown, Quebec, 1983.

Hanley, P., ed. *Earthcare: Ecological Agriculture in Saskatchewan*. Wynward, Saskatchewan: Earthcare Group, 1980.

Hearne, S. *Harvest of Unknowns: Pesticide Contamination in Imported Foods*. New York: Natural Resource Defence Council, 1984. Available from 122 E. 42nd Street, New York, New York 10168.

Jackson, Wes. *New Roots for Agriculture*. Omaha: University of Nebraska Press, 1985.

Kneen, Brewster. *From Land to Mouth: Understanding the Food System*. Toronto: NC Press, 1989.

Mitchell, Don. *The Politics of Food*. Toronto: James Lorimer & Co., 1975.

Mott, Lawrie, and Karen Snyder. *Pesticide Alert: A Guide to Pesticides in Fruits and Vegetables*. San Francisco: Sierra Club Books, 1987.

Ontario Coalition to Preserve Foodlands and Christian Farmers Federation of Ontario. *For Friends of Foodland: A Citizen's Guide to Foodland Preservation*. Guelph, 1989.

Pim, Linda R. *Additive Alert: A Guide to Improving the Quality and Safety of the Food You Eat*. Toronto: Doubleday, 1986.

———. *The Invisible Additives: Environmental Contaminants in Our Food*. Toronto: Doubleday, 1981.

Robbins, John. *Diet for a New America*. New York: New American Library, 1987.

Schell, Orville. *Modern Meat: Antibiotics, Hormones and the Pharmaceutical Farm*. New York: Random House, 1984.

Warnock, John. *The Politics of Hunger: The Global Food System*. New York: Methuen, 1987.

———. *Profit Hungry: The Food Industry in Canada*. Vancouver: New Star Books, 1978.

Weir, David. *The Bhopal Syndrome: Pesticides, Environment, and Health*. San Francisco: Sierra Club Books, 1987.

Weir, David, and Mark Schapiro. *Circle of Poison: Pesticides and People in a Hungry World*. Institute for Food and Development Policy, 1981. Available from IFDP, 145 Ninth Street, San Francisco: California 94103.

Wendell, Berry. *The Unsettling of America: Culture and Agriculture*. San Francisco: Sierra, 1986.

Magazines/Newsletters

AgriScience: The Magazine of Agricultural Science. Agricultural Institute of Canada/Agrican Publishers Inc., Suite 907, 151 Slater Street, Ottawa, Ontario K1P 5H4; (613) 232-9459. Monthly.

Biocontrol News. Agriculture Canada, Biosystematics Research Centre, Ottawa, Ontario K1A 0C7. Quarterly.

COGnition , Canadian Organic Growers (see source list of groups for address). Quarterly.

Earthkeeping. Christian Farmers Federations of Ontario and Alberta (see source list). Quarterly.

Harrowsmith. Telemedia Publishing Inc., 7 Queen Victoria Road, Camden East, Ontario K0K 1J0; (613) 378-6661. Six issues a year.

Humus. Mouvement pour l'agriculture biologique (see source list). Six issues a year.

The New Farm. Rodale Press, 222 Main Street, Emmaus, Pennsylvania 18098. Seven issues a year.

Pesticides and You. National Coalition Against the Misuse of Pesticides, 530 — 7th Street S.E., Washington, D.C. 20003; (202) 543-5450. Five issues a year.

CHAPTER 9
WILDERNESS: NO PLACE TO GO

Groups

Alberta Wilderness Association
Box 6398, Station D
Calgary, Alberta T2P 2E1
(403) 283-2025

Atlantic Center for the Environment
Suite 1900
600, rue de la Gauchetière Ouest
Montréal, Québec H3B 4L8
(514) 843-8297

B.C. Conservation Foundation
Fraser Highway
Langley, British Columbia V0X 1A0
(604) 533-2616

B.C. Wildlife Federation
5659 — 176th Street
Surrey, British Columbia V3S 4C5
(604) 576-8288

Canadian Nature Federation
453 Sussex Drive
Ottawa, Ontario K1N 6Z4
(613) 238-6154

Canadian Parks and Wilderness Society
160 Bloor Street East
Suite 1150
Toronto, Ontario M4W 1B9
(416) 972-0868

Canadian Wildlife Federation
1673 Carling Avenue
Ottawa, Ontario K2A 1C4
(604) 725-2191

Canadians for Responsible Northern Development
11911 University Avenue
Edmonton, Alberta T6G 1Z6
(403) 439-2972

Cariboo Horse Loggers Association
P.O. Box 4321
Quessnel, British Columbia V2J 3J3
(604) 747-3363

Conservation Council of Ontario
489 College Street
Suite 506
Toronto, Ontario M6G 1A5
(416) 969-9637

Ducks Unlimited
11-311 9th Street East
Box 818
Brooks, Alberta T0J 0J0
(403) 362-4827

Ecology North
Box 2888
Yellowknife, Northwest Territories X1A 2R2
(403) 873-6019

Federation of Alberta Naturalists
Box 1472
Edmonton, Alberta T5J 2N5
(403) 453-8629

The Federation of British Columbia Naturalists
321 — 1367 West Broadway
Vancouver, British Columbia V6H 4A9
(604) 737-3057

Federation of Ontario Naturalists
355 Lesmill Road
Don Mills, Ontario M3B 2W8
(416) 444-8419

Forests for Tomorrow
355 Lesmill Road
Don Mills, Ontario M3B 2W8
(416) 444-8419

Friends of Ecological Reserves
P.O. Box 1721, Station E
Victoria, British Columbia V8W 2Y1
(604) 386-8644

Friends of the North
8631—109 Street
Suite 211
Edmonton, Alberta T6G 1E8
(403) 439-4289

Island Nature Trust
P.O. Box 265
Charlottetown, Prince Edward Island C1A 7K4
(902) 892-7513

Islands Protection Society
Box 557
Masset, British Columbia V0T 1M0
(604) 626-5015

Manitoba Naturalists' Society
302—128 James Avenue
Winnipeg, Manitoba R3B 0N8
(204) 943-9029

The Natural Heritage League and the Ontario Heritage
Foundation
77 Bloor Street West
Toronto, Ontario M7A 2R9
(416) 965-8199

Natural History Society of Newfoundland and Labrador
P.O. Box 1013
St. John's, Newfoundland A1C 5M3

The Nature Conservancy of Canada
794A Broadview Avenue
Toronto, Ontario M4K 2P7
(416) 469-1701

The Nature Trust of British Columbia
100 Park Royal South
Suite 909
West Vancouver, British Columbia V7T 1A2
(604) 925-1128

New Brunswick Federation of Naturalists
277 Douglas Avenue
Saint John, New Brunswick E2K 1E5

New Brunswick Wildlife Federation
887 Union Street
Fredericton, New Brunswick E3A 3P7

Newfoundland Wilderness Society
Box 5132
St. John's, Newfoundland A1C 5V5

Northwest Wildlife Preservation Society
P.O. Box 34129
Station D
Vancouver, British Columbia V6J 4N3
(604) 736-8750

Nova Scotia Wildlife Federation
P.O. Box 654
Halifax, Nova Scotia B3J 2T3

Prairie for Tomorrow
c/o Department of Forest Science
855 General Services Building
University of Alberta
Edmonton, Alberta T6G 2H1
(403) 492-4413

Saskatchewan Natural History Society
Box 4348
Regina, Saskatchewan S4P 3W6
(306) 780-9273

Saskatchewan Wildlife Federation
Box 788
Moose Jaw, Saskatchewan S6H 4P5
(306) 692-8812

Sierra Club of Eastern Canada
2316 Queen Street East
Toronto, Ontario M4E 1G8
(416) 698-8446

Sierra Club of Western Canada
620 View Street
Suite 314
Victoria, British Columbia V8W 1J6
(604) 386-5255

Société canadienne pour la conservation de la nature
2597, rue Monsabre
Montreal, Quebec H1N 2K7
(514) 256-2545

Société pour la prévention de la cruauté envers les animaux
5215, Jean Talon Ouest
Montréal, Québec H4P 1X4
(514) 735-2711

Société québécoise pour la défense des animaux
1645, de Maisonneuve Ouest
Montréal, Québec H1S 1Z6
(514) 932-4260

Union québécoise de la conservation de la nature
160—76 Street East
Charlesbourg, Quebec G1H 7H6
(418) 628-9600

Valhalla Society
Box 224
New Denver, British Columbia V0G 1S0
(604) 358-2449

Western Canada Wilderness Committee
20 Water Street
Vancouver, British Columbia V6B 1A4
(604) 683-8220

Wildlife Habitat Canada
301—1704 Carling Avenue
Ottawa, Ontario K2A 1C7
(613) 722-2090

World Wildlife Fund
60 St. Clair Avenue East
Suite 201
Toronto, Ontario M4T 1N5
(416) 923-8173

Yukon Conservation Society
Box 4163
Whitehorse, Yukon Y1A 3T3
(403) 668-5678

Programs and Institutions

Canadian Plant Conservation Program
Devonian Botanic Garden
University of Alberta
Edmonton, Alberta T6G 2E1
(403) 987-3054

Long Point Bird Observatory
P.O. Box 160
Port Rowan, Ontario N0E 1M0
(519) 586-3531

Reptile Breeding Foundation
P.O. Box 1450
Picton, Ontario K0K 2T0
(613) 476-3351

St. Lawrence National Institute of Ecotoxicology
310, avenue des Ursulines
Rimouski, Quebec G5L 3A1
(418) 724-1746

Books

Berger, Thomas R. *Northern Frontier, Northern Homeland: The Report of the MacKenzie Valley Pipeline Inquiry*. Vancouver: Douglas & McIntyre, 1988.

Burnett, J. A., T. C. Dauphine, S. H. McCrindle, T. Mosquin, and C. Savage. *On the Brink: Endangered Species in Canada*. Saskatoon: Western Producer Prairie Books, 1989.

Cohen, Michael. *How Nature Works: Regenerating Kinship with Planet Earth*. Walpole, New Hampshire: Stillpoint Publishing, 1988.

Davies, Brian. *Red Ice: My Fight to Save the Seals*. Toronto: General, 1989.

Diamond, A. W., R. Bateman and R. L. Schreiber. *Save the Birds*. St. John's: Breakwater, 1989.

Drushka, Ken. *Stumped: The Forest Industry in Transition*. Vancouver: Douglas and McIntyre, 1985.

Fitzharris, Tim, and John A. Livingston. *Canada: A Natural History*. Markham, Ontario: Viking, 1988.

Foster, Janet. *Working for Wildlife: The Beginning of Preservation in Canada*. Toronto: University of Toronto Press, 1978.

George, Paul, et al. *Meares Island: Protecting a Natural Paradise*. Vancouver: Western Canada Wilderness Committee, 1986.

Hammond, Herb. *Forests? Forever?* Vancouver: Western Canada Wilderness Committee, 1990.

Hummel, Monte, ed. *Endangered Spaces*. Toronto: Key Porter Books, 1989.

Lawrence, R.D. *Canada's National Parks*. Toronto: Collins, 1983.

———. *The Natural History of Canada*. Toronto: Key Porter, 1988.

Livingston, John A. *The Fallacy of Wildlife Conservation*. Toronto: McClelland & Stewart, 1981.

———. *One Cosmic Instant: A Natural History of Human Arrogance*. Toronto: McClelland & Stewart, 1973.

Lovelock, James. *Gaia: A New Look at Life on Earth*. London: Oxford University Press, 1979.

Maser, Chris. *The Redesigned Forest*. San Pedro, California: R. & E. Miles, 1988.

M'Gonigle, Michael, and Wendy Wickwire. *Stein: The Way of the River*. Vancouver: Talon, 1988.

National Wetlands Working Group. *Wetlands of Canada*. Montreal: Polyscience Publications, 1988.

Sadler, Doug. *Reading Nature's Clues: A Guide to the Wild*. Peterborough, Ontario: Broadview Press, 1987.

Stephenson, Marylee. *Canada's National Parks: A Visitor's Guide*. Scarborough: Prentice-Hall, 1983.

Swift, Jamie. *Cut and Run: The Assault on Canada's Forests*. Toronto: Between the Lines, 1983.

Vessel, Matthew F., and Herbert H. Wong. *Natural History of Vacant Lots*. Berkeley: University of California Press, 1988.

Ward, Neville, and Beth Killham. *Heritage Conservation — The Natural Environment*. Waterloo: University of Waterloo Heritage Resource Centre, 1988.

Young, Cameron. *The Forests of British Columbia*. Vancouver: Whitecap, 1985.

Magazines/Newsletters

Borealis. Canadian Parks and Wilderness Society (see source list of groups for address). Quarterly.

Canadian Geographic. The Royal Canadian Geographical Society. Available from 39 McArthur Avenue, Vanier, Ontario K1L 8L7; 1-800-267-0824. Bi-monthly.

Canadian Plant Conservation Programme Newsletter. Available from Devonian Botanic Garden, University of Alberta, Edmonton, Alberta T6G 2E1; (403) 987-3054. Biannual.

The Country Side. Available from R.R. 1, Terra Cotta, Ontario L0P 1N0; (416) 838-2800. Quarterly.

Equinox. Telemedia Publishing Inc., 7 Queen Victoria Road, Camden East, Ontario K0K 1J0. (613) 378-6661. Bimonthly.

International Wildlife. Canadian Wildlife Federation (see source list of groups for address). Bimonthly.

Nature Canada. Canadian Nature Federation (see source list of groups for address). Quarterly.

Screef: Views From the Slash. B.C. Forestry News, P.O. Box 3352, Vancouver Main PO, Vancouver, British Columbia V6B 3Y3.

Sierra. Sierra Club (see source list of groups for address). Bi-monthly.

The Two-Bit News. Cariboo Horse Loggers Association (see source list). Quarterly.

Chapter 10
Home:
Getting Our Own Houses in Order

Groups

Friends of the Earth
251 Laurier Avenue West
Suite 701
Ottawa, Ontario K1P 5J6
(613) 230-3352

Greenpeace Canada
2623 West 4th Avenue
Vancouver, British Columbia V6K 1P8
(604) 736-0321

Greenpeace Montreal
2444, Notre Dame Ouest
Montréal, Québec H3J 1N5
(514) 933-0021

Greenpeace Toronto
578 Bloor Street West
2nd Floor
Toronto, Ontario M6G 1K1
(416) 538-6470

Pollution Probe
12 Madison Avenue
Toronto, Ontario M5R 2S1
(416) 926-1907

Society Promoting Environmental Conservation
2150 Maple Street
Vancouver, British Columbia V6J 3T3
(604) 736-7732

Ecology Action Centre
3115 Veith Street
Halifax, Nova Scotia B3K 3G9
(902) 454-7828

Conservation Council of New Brunswick
180 St. John Street
Fredericton, New Brunswick E3B 4A9
(506) 458-8747

Institutions with Information on Animal Use in Product Research

The Toronto Humane Society
11 River Street
Toronto, Ontario M5A 4C2
(416) 392-2273

The Canadian Federation of Humane Societies
30 Concourse Gate
Suite 102
Nepean, Ontario K2E 7V7
(613) 224-8072

People for the Ethical Treatment of Animals
P.O. Box 42516
Washington, D.C. 20015
(301) 770-7444

Beauty Without Cruelty
175 West 12th Street
New York, New York 10011-8275
(212) 989-8073

Books

Household Alternatives to Chemicals

Christensen, Karen. *Home Ecology*. London, England: Arlington Books, 1989.

Dadd, Debra Lynn. *Non-Toxic and Natural: How to Avoid Dangerous Everyday Products and Buy or Make Safe Ones*. New York: St. Martin's Press, 1984.

————. *The Non-Toxic Home: Protecting Yourself and Your Family From Everyday Toxics and Health Hazards*. New York: St. Martin's Press, 1986.

Harmony Foundation. *The Environmentally Friendly Consumer: Home and Family*. Ottawa, 1989. Available from 19 Oakvale Avenue, Ottawa, Ontario K1Y 3S3; (613) 230-7353.

Hupping, Carol, Cheryl Winters Tetreau and Roger B. Yepsen, Jr., eds. *Rodale's Book of Hints, Tips and Everyday Wisdom*. Emmaus, Pennsylvania: Rodale Press, 1985.

Richman, Beth, and Susan Hassol. *Creating a Healthy World: 101 Practical Tips for Home and Work*. Snowmass, Colorado: The Windstar Foundation, 1989.

Rousseau, David, W.J. Rea and Jean Enright. *Your Home, Your Health, and Well-Being*. Vancouver: Hartley & Marks, 1987.

Troyer, Warner, and Glenys Moss. *The Canadian Green Consumer Guide*. Toronto: McClelland and Stewart, 1989.

Wallace, Dan, ed. *The Natural Formula Book for Home and Yard*. Emmaus, Pennsylvania: Rodale Press, 1982.

Non-Toxic Chemical Control

Society Promoting Environmental Conservation. *Pest or Guest: A Guide to Alternative Pest Control in the Home and Garden*. Available from 2150 Maple Street, Vancouver, British Columbia V6J 3T3; (604) 736-7732.

Integrated Pest Management for the Home and Garden. Available from the Institute for Environmental Studies, 408 South Goodwin Avenue, Urbana, Illinois 61801.

Magazines/Newsletters

Common Sense Pest Control Quarterly. Bio-Integral Resource Centre, P.O. Box 7414, Berkeley, California 94707. Quarterly.

Pesticides and You. National Coalition Against the Misuse of Pesticides, 530 — 7th Street SE, Washington, DC 20003. Five issues a year.

CHAPTER 11
GARBAGE: TRIM THAT TONNE

Groups

Canadian Organic Growers
P.O. Box 6408, Station J
Ottawa, Ontario K2A 3Y6
(613) 259-2967

Ecological Agriculture Projects
P.O. Box 191
Macdonald College
21, 111 Lakeshore Road
Ste-Anne-de-Bellevue, Quebec H9X 1C0
(514) 398-7771

Provincial Recycling Councils
(See source list for Chapter 6, "Garbage: Our Gross National
Product," for addresses.)

Diaper Services

Babykins Canada Ltd.
Unit 4
3531 Jacombs Road
Richmond, British Columbia V6V 1Z8
(604) 270-6116

Stork Diaper Service
2515 Eastbrook Parkway
Vancouver, British Columbia V5C 5W2
(604) 291-2229

Worldwide Baby Basics Inc.
491 Pacific Boulevard
Vancouver, British Columbia V6B 5G6
(604) 685-8125

Cherub Diaper Service
2911 Queenston Street
Victoria, British Columbia V8R 4P4
(604) 592-3144

Daisy Fresh Diaper Service
2584 Quadra Street
Victoria, British Columbia V9C 2C6
(604) 381-2729

Baby Love Products
5015 — 46 Street
Camrose, Alberta T4V 3G3
(403) 672-1763

Daisy Fresh Diaper Service
11035 — 101 Street
Grande Prairie, Alberta T8V 2R7
(403) 338-2288

Stork Diaper Service
12547 — 129 Street
Edmonton, Alberta T5L 1C8
(403) 452-5046

Stork Diaper Service
5728—35 Street E.
Calgary, Alberta T2C 2G5
(403) 279-2900

Jack & Jill Diaper Service
10 Wilkie Road
Regina, Saskatchewan S4S 5Y2
(306) 585-0123

Tidy Diaper Service
Bay 10 — 1622, Ontario Avenue
Saskatoon, Saskatchewan S7K 1S8
(306) 664-4100

Stork Diaper Service
1860 King Edward Street
Winnipeg, Manitoba R2R 0N2
(204) 633-5522

After the Stork Diaper Service Ltd.
589 Middlefield Road
Unit 19
Scarborough, Ontario M1V 3S3
(416) 754-7462

Born to Love
21 Potsdam Road
Number 61
Downsview, Ontario M3N 1N3
(416) 663-7143

Bottom's Up Diaper Service
58 Corinne Crescent
Scarborough, Ontario M1K 2Y9
(416) 752-0022

Comfy Cotton Diaper Service
860 Denison Street, Unit 7
Markham, Ontario L3R 4H1
(416) 940-8118

Toronto Diaper Service
5359 Timberlea Blvd.
Mississauga, Ontario L4W 4N5
(416) 624-2229

Friendly Diaper Service
P.O. Box 373
Belleville, Ontario K8N 5A5
(613) 966-7033

Ottawa Diaper Service Inc.
850 Campbell Avenue
Ottawa, Ontario K2A 1J4
(613) 728-0921

Darcie Lee Linens Inc.
5750 Thimens Blvd.
Montreal, Quebec H4R 2K9
(514) 335-3675

Books

Bem, Robyn. *Everyone's Guide to Home Composting*. New York: Van Nostrand Reinhold, 1978.

Campbell, Stu. *Let it Rot! The Home Gardener's Guide to Composting*. Charlotte, Vermont: Garden Way, 1975.

Catton, Chris, and James Gray. *The Incredible Heap: A Guide to Compost Gardening*. New York: St. Martin's Press, 1983.

Minnick, Jerry, Marjorie Hunt and the editors of *Organic Gardening Magazine*. *The Rodale Guide to Composting*. Emmaus, Pennsylvania: Rodale Press, 1979.

CHAPTER 12
ENERGY: TURNING ON EFFICIENCY

Groups

Biomass Energy Institute Inc.
1329 Niakwa Road East
Winnipeg, Manitoba R2J 3T4
(204) 257-3891

Canadian Coalition for Nuclear Responsibility
P.O. Box 236
Snowdon
Montreal, Quebec H3X 3T4
(514) 489-2665

Canadian Solar Industries Association
67A Sparks Street
Ottawa, Ontario K1P 5A5
(613) 237-7000

Canadian Wind Energy Association
44A Clarey Avenue
Ottawa, Ontario K1S 2R7
(613) 234-9463

Canadian Wood Energy Institute
85 West Wilmot Street, Unit 5
Richmond Hill, Ontario L4B 1K7
(416) 886-9247

Energy Probe
225 Brunswick Avenue
Toronto, Ontario M5S 2M6
(416) 978-7014

Friends of the Earth
251 Laurier Avenue West
Suite 701
Ottawa, Ontario K1P 5J6
(613) 230-3352

Greenpeace Canada
2623 West 4th Avenue
Vancouver, British Columbia V6K 1P8
(604) 736-0321

Greenpeace Toronto
578 Bloor Street West, 2nd Floor
Toronto, Ontario M6G 1K1
(416) 538-6470

Greenpeace Montreal
2444, Notre Dame Ouest
Montréal, Québec H3J 1N5
(514) 933-0021

Nuclear Awareness Project
Box 2331
Oshawa, Ontario L1H 7V4
(416) 725-1565

Public Citizen
Critical Mass Energy Project
215 Pennsylvania Avenue SE
Washington, D.C. 20036
(202) 546-4996

Rocky Mountain Institute
1739 Snowmass Creek Road
Old Snowmass, Colorado 81654-999
(303) 927-3851

Solar Energy Society of Canada
15 York Street
Suite 3
Ottawa, Ontario K1N 5S7
(613) 236-4594

Government Ministries

At the Federal Level
Prime Minister of Canada
House of Commons
Ottawa, Ontario K1A 0A2
(no postage necessary)

Minister of Energy, Mines & Resources
House of Commons
Ottawa, Ontario K1A 0A2
(no postage necessary)

At the Provincial Level
Minister of Mines and Energy
P.O. Box 4750
St. John's, Newfoundland A1C 5T7

Minister of Mines and Energy
P.O. Box 1087
Halifax, Nova Scotia B3J 2X1

Minister of Natural Resources
P.O. Box 6000
Fredericton, New Brunswick E3B 5H1

Minister of Energy and Forestry
P.O. Box 2000
Charlottetown, Prince Edward Island C1A 7N8

Ministère de l'Énergie et des Ressources
200, chemin Ste Foy, 7e-étage,
Québec, Québec G1R 4X7

Minister of Natural Resources and Energy
56 Wellesley Street West, 12th Floor
Toronto, Ontario M7A 2B7

Minister of Energy and Mines
301 Legislative Building
Winnipeg, Manitoba R3C 0V8

Minister of Energy and Mines
Legislative Building
Regina, Saskatchewan S4S 0B3

Minister of Energy
Room 407, Legislative Building
Edmonton, Alberta T5K 2B6

Minister of Energy, Mines and Petroleum Resources
Room 133, Parliament Buildings
Victoria, British Columbia V8K 1X4

Minister of Economic Development: Mines and Small Business
P.O. Box 2703
Whitehorse, Yukon Y1A 2C6

Minister of Energy, Mines and Petroleum Resources
P.O. Box 1320
Yellowknife, Northwest Territories X1A 2L9

Books

Babin, Ronald. *The Nuclear Power Game*. Montreal: Black Rose Books, 1985.

Bertell, Rosalie. *No Immediate Danger? Prognosis For a Radioactive Earth*. Toronto: Women's Press, 1985.

Bott, Robert, David Books and John Robinson. *Life After Oil: A Renewable Energy Policy for Canada*. Edmonton: Hurtig, 1983.

Brooks, D. *Zero Energy Growth for Canada*. Toronto: McClelland and Stewart, 1981.

Caufield, Catherine. *Multiple Exposures: Chronicles of the Radiation Age*. Toronto: Stoddart, 1989.

Finch, Ron. *Exporting Danger: A History of the Canadian Nuclear Energy Export Programme*. Montreal: Black Rose Books, 1986.

Flagler, Gordon. *Canadian Wood Heat Book*. Ottawa: Deneau and Greenberg, 1979.

Friends of the Earth. *2025: Soft Energy Futures for Canada*. Edmonton: Hurtig, 1983.

GATT-Fly. *Power to Choose: Canada's Energy Options*. Toronto: Between the Lines, 1981.

Gyorgy, Anna. *No Nukes: Everyone's Guide to Nuclear Power*. Montreal: Black Rose Books, 1979.

Hassol, Susan, and Beth Richman. *Energy: 101 Practical Tips for Home and Work*. Snowmass, Colorado: Windstar Foundation, 1989.

Lovins, Amory. *Soft Energy Paths*. Toronto: Fitzhenry & Whiteside, 1979.

Marmorek, Jan. *Over a Barrel: A Guide to the Canadian Energy Crisis*. Toronto: Doubleday, 1981.

Marples, David R. *The Social Impact of the Chernobyl Disaster*. Edmonton: University of Alberta Press, 1988.

McKay, Paul. *Electric Empire: The Inside Story of Ontario Hydro*. Toronto: Between the Lines, 1983.

Poch, David. *Radiation Alert: A Consumer's Guide to Radiation*. Toronto: Doubleday, 1985.

Reece, Ray. *The Sun Betrayed: A Study of the Corporate Seizure of Solar Power Development*. Montreal: Black Rose Books, 1979.

Robbins, W. *Getting the Shaft: The Radioactive Waste Controversy in Manitoba*. Winnipeg: Queenston House, 1984.

Sanger, Penny. *Blind Faith: The Nuclear Industry in One Small Town*. Toronto: McGraw-Hill Ryerson, 1981.

Solomon, Lawrence. *Energy Shock: After the Oil Runs Out*. Toronto: Doubleday. 1980.

————. *Power at What Cost? Breaking Up Ontario Hydro's Monopoly*. Toronto: Doubleday, 1984.

Magazines/Newsletters

Bio-Joule. Biomass Energy Institute (see list of groups above for address). Bi-monthly.

Canadian Energy Education Newsletter. Alberta Department of Energy, Energy Conservation Branch, Highfield Place, 2nd Floor, 10010-106 Street, Edmonton, Alberta T5J 3L8; (403) 427-5200. Quarterly.

Critical Mass Energy Bulletin. Public Citizen (see list of groups above for address). Bi-monthly.

Harrowsmith. Telemedia Publishing Inc., 7 Queen Victoria Road, Camden East, Ontario K0K 1J0; (613) 378-6661. Six issues a year.

Renewable Energy News. Solar Age, Box 470, Peterborough, New Hampshire 03458-0470. Monthly.

Rocky Mountain Institute Newsletter. Rocky Mountain Institute, 1739 Snowmass Creek Road, Old Snowmass, Colorado 81654-999; (303) 927-3851. Quarterly.

Sol: The Voice of Renewable Energy in Canada. Solar Energy Society of Canada (see list of groups above for address). Bi-monthly.

CHAPTER 13
ENERGY CONSERVATION IN THE HOME

Groups, Associations, Institutions and Ministries

Building and Renovating For Energy Efficiency
Canadian Home Builders' Association
200 Elgin Street
Suite 702
Ottawa, Ontario K2P 1L5
(613) 563-3512

R-2000 Yukon
P.O. Box 5229
Whitehorse, Yukon Y1A 4Z2
(403) 668-2914

R-2000 Program
5004 — 54th Street
3rd Floor
Northern United Place
Yellowknife, Northwest Territories X1A 2R6
(403) 873-4556

Canadian Home Builders' Association of B.C.
37000 Willingdon Avenue
Burnaby, British Columbia V5G 3H2
(604) 432-7112

Alberta Home Builders' Association
205-10544—114th Street
Edmonton, Alberta T5H 3J7
(403) 424-5890

Saskatchewan Home Builders' Association
857 Arcola Avenue
Regina, Saskatchewan S4N 0S9
(306) 569-2424

Manitoba Home Builders' Association
239—1120 Grant Avenue
Winnipeg, Manitoba R3M 2A6
(204) 477-5110

Ontario Home Builders' Association
20 Upjohn Road
North York, Ontario M3B 2V9
(416) 447-0077

New Brunswick Home Builders' Association
280 Charlotte Street
Apt. 2
Fredericton, New Brunswick E3B 1L4
(506) 459-7219

R-2000 Regional Office
5151 George Street
Suite 503
Halifax, Nova Scotia B3J 1M5
(902) 454-2000

Construction Association of P.E.I.
Holland College Royalty Centre
Room 226
40 Enman Crescent
Charlottetown, Prince Edward Island C1A 7L3
(902) 368-3303

Newfoundland & Labrador Home Builders' Association
718 Water Street
St. John's, Newfoundland A1E 1C1
(709) 753-2049

Energy Conservation Contractors Warranty Corporation
6855 Meadowvale Town Centre Circle
Suite 202
Mississauga, Ontario L5N 2W1
(416) 567-4944
1-800-263-5974

Energy Conservation Contractors Warranty Corporation
(Associate Office)
P.O. Box 3214
Winnipeg, Manitoba R3C 4E7
(204) 783-1273

General Information on Energy Efficiency

Canadian Housing and Mortgage Corporation
682 Montreal Road
Ottawa, Ontario K1A 0P7
(613) 748-2000

Ecology House/Pollution Probe Foundation
12 Madison Avenue
Toronto, Ontario M5R 2S1
(416) 926-1907

Energy Information Centre
Society Promoting Environmental Conservation
2150 Maple Street
Vancouver, British Columbia V6J 3T3
(604) 736-7732

Environmental Resource Centre
10511 Saskatchewan Drive
Edmonton, Alberta T6E 4S1
(403) 433-4808

Radon

Canadian Institute for Radiation Safety
Suite 1050
595 Bay Street
Toronto, Ontario M5G 2C2
(416) 596-1617

alphaNUCLEAR Company
1125 Derry Road East
Mississauga, Ontario L5T 1P3
(416) 564-1383

R.A.D. Service and Instruments Ltd.
50 Silver Star Blvd.
Unit 208
Scarborough, Ontario M1V 3L3
(416) 298-9200

SCAT Science and Technology Inc.
191 Prospect Street
Fredericton, New Brunswick E3B 2T7
(506) 452-1414

Provincial Ministries Responsible for Radon Protection

Radiation Protection Service
British Columbia Ministry of Health
307 West Broadway
Suite 200
Vancouver, British Columbia V5Y 1P9
(604) 660-6630

Radiation Health Branch
Occupational Health and Safety Division
Community and Occupational Health
4th Floor, Donsdale Place
10709 Jasper Avenue
Edmonton, Alberta T5J 3N3
(403) 427-2691

Radiation Safety Unit
Department of Human Resources
Labour and Employment
Saskatchewan Place
1870 Albert Street
Regina, Saskatchewan S4P 3V4
(306) 787-4486

Radiation Protection Section
Department of Medical Physics
Manitoba Cancer Foundation
100 Olivia Street
Winnipeg, Manitoba R3E 0V9
(204) 787-2211

Radiation Protection Service
Ministry of Labour
40 University Avenue
8th Floor
Toronto, Ontario M7A 1T7
(416) 965-8178

Chef de la division de l'environnement du Québec
Suite 3860
5199 est, rue Sherbrooke
Montréal, Québec H1T 3X9
(514) 873-1978

Radiation Protection Services
Department of Health and Community Services
P.O. Box 5100
Fredericton, New Brunswick E3B 5G8
(506) 453-2067

Senior Radiation Health Officer
Department of Health
P.O. Box 488
Halifax, Nova Scotia B3H 2R8
(902) 424-4077

Radiology Manager
Queen Elizabeth Hospital
Charlottetown, Prince Edward Island C1A 8T5
(902) 566-6277

Radiation Health and Safety Services
Occupational Health and Safety Division
Government of Newfoundland and Labrador
Department of Labour and Manpower
Beothuck Building, Crosbie Place
St. John's, Newfoundland A1C 5T7
(709) 576-2645

Books

Energy Efficiency

Argue, Robert. *The Well-Tempered House: Energy Efficient Building for Cold Climates*. Toronto: Renewable Energy in Canada, 1980.

Conservation Council of New Brunswick. *Taking Control: A Soft Energy Path for New Brunswick*. Available from 180 St. John Street, Fredericton, New Brunswick E3B 4A9.

Herbert, Ralph. *Cut Your Electricity Bills in Half*. Emmaus, Pennsylvania: Rodale, 1986.

McGuigan, D. *Harnessing Water Power for Home Energy*. Charlotte, Vermont: Garden Way, 1978.

———. *Harnessing the Wind for Home Energy*. Charlotte, Vermont: Garden Way, 1978.

Mattock, Chris, Thomas Senchek, and John Raabe. *Superinsulated Design and Construction*. New York: Van Nostrand Reinhold, 1987.

Mazria, Edward. *The Passsive Solar Energy Book: A Complete Guide to Passive Solar Home, Greenhouse, and Building Design*. Emmaus, Pennsylvania: Rodale, 1979.

Mohr, Merilyn. *Sunwings: The Harrowsmith Guide to Solar Addition Architecture*. Camden East, Ontario: Camden House, 1985.

Ontario Ministry of Energy. *Streams of Power: Developing Small Scale Hydro Systems*. Scarborough: Firefly, 1986.

Shurcliff, William A. *Thermal Shutters and Shades: Over 100 Schemes Reducing Heat-Loss Through Windows*. Andover, Massachusetts: Brick House, 1980.

Steven Winter Associates. *Passive Solar Construction Handbook*. Emmaus, Pennsylvania: Rodale Press, 1983.

Wade, Alex. *A Design and Construction Handbook for Energy-Saving Houses*. Emmaus, Pennsylvania: Rodale, 1980.

Indoor Air Quality

Dadd, Debra Lynn. *The Non-Toxic Home: Protecting Yourself and Your Family from Everyday Toxins and Health Hazards*. New York: St. Martin's Press, 1986.

Good, Clint, and Debra Lynn Dadd. *Healthful Houses: How to Design and Build Your Own*. Bethesda, Maryland: Guaranty Press, 1988.

Hunter, Linda Mason. *The Healthy Home*. Emmaus, Pennsylvania: Rodale, 1989.

Kadulski, Richard. *Residential Ventilation: Achieving Indoor Air Quality*. Vancouver: Solplan Review, 1989. Available from Box 86627, North Vancouver, British Columbia V7L 4L2.

Small, Bruce. *Implications of Chemical Hypersensitivity for Housing Design*. Canada Housing and Mortgage Corporation. (See list of groups and agencies above for address.)

———. *Indoor Air Pollution and Housing Technology*. Canada Housing and Mortgage Corporation.

———. *The Susceptibility Report*. Goodwood, Ontario: Sunnyhill Research Foundation. Available from R.R. #1, Goodwood, Ontario L0C 1A0 .

Raab, Karl. *Strategies for Healthful Residential Environments*. Canada Housing and Mortgage Corporation. (See list of groups and agencies above for address.).

Rousseau, David, W.J. Rea and Jean Enright. *Your Home, Your Health and Well-Being*. Vancouver: Hartley & Marks, 1987.

Vischer, Jacqueline. *Environmental Quality in Offices*. New York: Van Nostrand Reinhold, 1989.

Radon

Cohen, Bernard. *Radon: A Homeowner's Guide to Detection and Control*. Consumer's Report Books, 1987.

LaFavore, Michael. *Radon: The Invisible Threat*. Emmaus, Pennsylvania: Rodale Press, 1987.

Booklets

Society Promoting Environmental Conservation. *A Homeowner's Guide to Energy Conservation*. Available from 2150 Maple Street, Vancouver, British Columbia V6J 3T3; (604) 736-SPEC.

Woodwell, John. *Water Efficiency for Your Home: Products and Advice Which Save Water, Energy and Money*. Available from the Rocky Mountain Institute, 1739 Snowmass Creek Road, Old Snowmass, Colorado 81654-999; (303) 927-3851.

Rocky Mountain Institute. *Practical Home Energy Savings*. Available from the Rocky Mountain Institute (address above).

Magazines

Harrowsmith. Telemedia Publishing Inc., 7 Queen Victoria Road, Camden East, Ontario K0K 1J0; (613) 378-6661. Six issues a year.

The Renovator. Available from Alberta Energy Conservation Branch, 2nd Floor, 10010-106 Street, Edmonton, Alberta T5J 3L8; (403) 427-5200. Quarterly.

Solplan Review: The Independent Newsletter of Energy Efficient Building Practice. Available from The Drawing-Room Graphic Services Ltd., Box 86627, North Vancouver, British Columbia V7L 4L2. Bi-monthly.

CHAPTER 14
GREEN CONSUMER

Groups

Consumers' Association of Canada
Box 9300
Ottawa, Ontario K1G 3T9
(613) 723-0187

Products

La Balance
1249, de Conde
Montréal, Québec H3K 2E4

Ecover
Mercantile Food Co.
Georgetown, Connecticut 06829
U.S.A.

Nature Clean
P.O. 248
West Hill, Ontario M1E 4R5

Soap Factory
141 Cushman Road
St. Catharines, Ontario L2M 6T2

Books

Product Information

Harmony Foundation. *The Home and Family Guide: Practical Action for the Environment*. Ottawa: Harmony Foundation, 1989. Available from 19 Oakvale Avenue, Ottawa, Ontario K1Y 3S3; (613) 230-7353 or any Royal Bank branch.

Pollution Probe Foundation. *The Canadian Green Consumer Guide*. Toronto: McClelland and Stewart, 1989.

Will, Rosalyn, Alice Tepper Marlin, Benjamin Corson and Jonathan Schorsch. *Shopping for a Better World*. New York: Council on Economic Priorities, 1989. Available from 30 Irving Place, New York, New York 10003; (212) 420-1133.

General

Elgin, Duane. *Voluntary Simplicity*. Scarborough: Prentice-Hall, 1980.

Henry, Jules. *Culture Against Man*. New York: McGraw, 1965.

Meadows, Donella H., ed. *The Limits to Growth*. New York: Universe Books, 1972.

Nickerson, Mike. *Bakavi: Change the World I Want to Stay On*. Merrickville, Ontario: The Bakavi School of Permaculture, 1977. Available from P.O. Box 374, Merrickville, Ontario K0G 1N0.

Seymour, John, and Herbert Girardet. *Blueprint for a Green Planet*. Scarborough: Prentice-Hall, 1987.

Solomon, Lawrence. *The Conserver Solution*. Toronto: Doubleday, 1978.

Magazines

Adbusters: The Magazine of Media and Environmental Strategies. The Media Foundation, 1381 Howard Avenue, Burnaby, British Columbia V5B 3S2; (604) 736-9401. Quarterly.

Canadian Consumer. Consumers' Association of Canada, Box 9300, Ottawa, Ontario K1G 3T9; (613) 723-0187. Monthly.

Probe Post. Pollution Probe Foundation, 12 Madison Avenue, Toronto, Ontario M5R 2S1; (416) 926-1907. Quarterly.

Whole Earth Review. P.O. Box 38 Sansalito, California 94966-9932; (415) 332-1716. Quarterly.

Alternative Investing

Funds
Environmental Investment Funds
Energy Probe
225 Brunswick Avenue
Toronto, Ontario M5S 2M6
(416) 978-7014

Ethical Growth Fund
Vancouver City Savings Credit Union
515 West 10th Avenue
Vancouver, British Columbia V5Z 4A8
(604) 877-7000

Summa Fund
Investors Group
447 Portage Avenue
Winnipeg, Manitoba R3C 3B6
(204) 943-0361

Organizations
Canadian Centre for Ethics and Corporate Policy
George Brown House
50 Baldwin Street
2nd Floor
Toronto, Ontario M5T 1L4
(416) 348-8691

Canadian Social Investment Study Group
Suite 712
151 Slater Street
Ottawa, Ontario K1P 5H3
(613) 230-5221

EthicScan
P.O. Box 165
Station S
Toronto, Ontario M5M 4L7
(416) 783-6776

Taskforce on the Churches and Corporate Responsibility
129 St. Clair Avenue West
Toronto, Ontario M4V 1N5
(416) 923-1758

Books

Domini, A., and Kinder, P. *Ethical Investing*. Reading, Massachusetts: Addison-Wesley, 1986.

Ellmen, Eugene. *How to Invest Your Money With a Clear Conscience*. Toronto: James Lorimer & Co., 1987.

———. *The 1989 Canadian Guide to Profitable Ethical Investing*. Toronto: James Lorimer & Co., 1989.

Lyndenberg, S.D., A.T. Marlin, and S.O. Strub. *Rating America's Corporate Conscience*. Reading, Massachusetts: Addison-Wesley, 1986.

Meeker-Lowry, Susan. *Economics As If the Earth Really Mattered: A Catalyst Guide to Socially Conscious Investing*. Santa Cruz: New Society Press, 1988.

Olive, David. *Just Rewards*. Markham: Penguin, 1988.

Ward, S. *Socially Responsible Investment*. London: Directory of Social Change and Ethical Investment Research and Information Service, 1986.

Magazines and Newsletters

Canadian Alternative Investments Newsletter. New North Finance, 3—159 Dunn Avenue, Toronto, Ontario M6K 2R8. Bi-monthly.

The Corporate Ethics Monitor. Carswell, 2330 Midland Avenue, Agincourt, Ontario M1S 1P7. Bi-monthly.

Management Ethics. Canadian Centre for Ethics and Corporate Policy, Toronto-Dominion Centre, Suite 204, P.O. Box 175, Commercial Union Tower, Toronto, Ontario M5K 1H6.

CHAPTER 16
YARD AND GARDEN:
GREENING YOUR OWN BACKYARD

Groups

Canadian Organic Growers
Box 6408, Station J
Ottawa, Ontario K2A 3Y6
(613) 259-2967

Canadian Wildflower Society
35 Bauer Crescent
Unionville, Ontario L3R 4H3

City Farmer
801-318 Homer Street
Vancouver, British Columbia V6B 2V3
(604) 685-5832

Ecological Agriculture Projects
Box 191, Macdonald College
21, 111 Lakeshore Road
Ste-Anne-de-Bellevue, Quebec H9X 1C0
(514) 398-7771

Ecology Park
12 Madison Avenue
Toronto, Ontario M5R 2S1
(416) 926-1907

Friends of the Earth
251 Laurier Avenue West
Suite 701
Ottawa, Ontario K1P 5J6
(613) 230-3352

Urban Wilderness Gardeners
227 Kenilworth Avenue
Toronto, Ontario M41 3S7

Provincial Agriculture Ministries

Ministry of Agriculture and Fisheries
Parliament Building
Victoria, British Columbia V8W 2Z7
(604) 387-5121

Department of Agriculture
Agriculture Building
7000 — 113th Street
Edmonton, Alberta T6H 5T6
(403) 427-2727

Department of Agriculture
Walter Scott Building
Regina, Saskatchewan S4S 0B1
(306) 787-5035

Department of Agriculture
165 Legislative Building
Winnipeg, Manitoba R3C 0V8
(204) 945-3722

Ministry of Agriculture and Food
801 Bay Street
Toronto, Ontario M7A 1A3
(416) 965-1421

Ministère de l'Agriculture, des pêcheries et de l'alimentation
200-A, ch. Ste-Foy, Québec, Québec G1R 4X6
(418) 643-2673

Department of Agriculture
Box 6000
Fredericton, New Brunswick E3B 5H1
(506) 453-2666

Department of Agriculture and Marketing
World Trade and Convention Centre
5th Floor, 1800 Argyle Street
Box 190
Halifax, Nova Scotia B3J 2M4
(902) 424-6734

Department of Agriculture
Jones Building, 4th Floor
11 Kent Street, Box 2000
Charlottetown, Prince Edward Island C1A 7N8
(902) 368-4880

Department of Rural, Agricultural and Northern Development
Confederation Building
West Block, 4th Floor
St. John's Newfoundland A1C 5T7
(709) 576-3200

Books

General Lawn and Garden Care

Ball, Jeff. *Rodale's Garden Problem Solver: Vegetables, Fruits and Herbs*. Emmaus, Pennsylvania: Rodale Press, 1988.

Bennett, Jennifer. *The Harrowsmith Gardener's Guide to Ground Covers*. Camden East, Ontario: Camden House, 1987.

———. *The Harrowsmith Northern Gardener*. Camden East, Ontario: Camden House, 1988.

Foster, Catherine Osgood. *Building Healthy Gardens*. Charlotte, Vermont: Garden Way, 1989.

Franklin, Stuart. *Building a Healthy Lawn: A Safe and Natural Approach*. Charlotte, Vermont: Garden Way, 1988.

Gershuny, Grace, and Joseph Smillie. *The Soul of Soil: A Guide to Ecological Soil Management*. Erle, Quebec: Gaia Services. Available from R.R. #1, Weedon, Erie, Quebec J0B 3J0.

Munroe, Glenn. *The Growing City: A Guide to Urban Community Gardening In Toronto*. Toronto: Ontario Public Interest Research Group, 1986.

Ogden, Samuel. *Step-by-Step to Organic Vegetable Growing*. Emmaus, Pennsylvania: Rodale Press, 1975.

The Organic Way to Mulching. Emmaus, Pennsylvania: Rodale Press, 1971.

Rodale, Robert, ed. *The Basic Book of Organic Gardening*. New York: Ballantine, 1987.

Rubin, Carole. *How to Get Your Lawn and Garden Off Drugs*. Ottawa: Friends of the Earth, 1989.

Schultz, Warren. *The Chemical-Free Lawn: The Newest Varieties and Techniques to Grow Lush, Hardy Grass*. Emmaus, Pennsylvania: Rodale, 1989.

Taylor's Guide to Groundcovers. Markham, Ontario: Thomas Allen & Sons, 1986.

Wallace, Dan. *The Natural Formula Book for Home and Yard*. Emmaus, Pennsylvania: Rodale Press, 1982.

Yepsen, Robert B., Jr., ed. *Organic Plant Protection*. Emmaus, Pennsylvania. Rodale Press, 1976.

Landscaping With Native Species

Baines, Chris. *How to Make a Wildlife Garden*. London, England: Hamish Hamilton, 1987.

Crockett, James, O.E. Allen and the editors of Time-Life Books. *Wildflower Gardening*. Alexandria, Virginia: Time-Life Books, 1977.

Dickelman, J., and R. Shuster. *Natural Landscaping: Designing With Native Plant Communities*. New York: McGraw Hill, 1982.

Dorney, Robert. *A Guide to Natural Woodland and Prairie Gardening*. Waterloo, Ontario: Natural Woodland Nursery Ltd.

Emery, Malcolm. *Promoting Nature in Cities and Towns: A Practical Guide*. London, England: Croom Helm, 1986.

Minnesota Department of Natural Resources. *Landscaping for Wildlife*. Available from Documents Division, 117 University Avenue, St. Paul, Minnesota 55155.

Sperka, Maria. *Growing Wildflowers*. New York: Charles Scribner and Sons, 1984.

Vessel, Mathew F., and Herbert H. Wong. *Natural History of Vacant Lots*. Berkeley: University of California Press, 1988.

Young, J.A., and C. Young. *Collecting, Processing and Germinating Seeds of Wildplants*. Portland: Timber Press, 1986.

Companion Planting

Philbrick, H., and R.B. Gregg. *Companion Plants and How to Use Them*. New York: Devin-Adair, 1966.

Riotte, Lousie. *Carrots Love Tomatoes: Secrets of Companion Planting for Successful Gardening*. Charlotte, Vermont: Garden Way, 1976.

Roses Love Garlic: Secrets of Companion Planting with Flowers. Charlotte, Vermont: Garden Way, 1983.

Organic Orchards

Hall-Beyer, Bart, and J. Richard. *Ecological Fruit Production in the North*. Scotstown, Quebec: 1983.

Logsdon, Gene. *Organic Orcharding*. Emmaus, Pennsylvania: Rodale Press, 1981.

Page, Stephen, and Joseph Smillie. *The Orchard Almanac: A Spraysaver Guide*. Erle, Quebec: Spraysaver Publications, 1986.

Pest Identification and Control

Bird, David M. *City Critters*. Montreal: Eden Press, 1986.

Carr, Anna, and Miranda Smith. *Rodale's Garden Insect, Disease and Weed Identification Guide*. Emmaus, Pennsylvania: Rodale Press, 1988.

Hyer, Bruce. *The Gypsy Moth: A Handbook for Cottagers and Homeowners*. Toronto: Pollution Probe, 1987.

Institute for Environmental Studies, University of Illinois. *Integrated Pest Management for the Home and Garden*. Urbana-Champaign. Available from Institute for Environmental Studies, 408 South Goodwin Avenue, Urbana, Illinois, U.S.A. 61801.

Philbrick, Helen, and John Philbrick. *The Bug Book: Harmless Insect Controls*. Charlotte, Vermont: Garden Way Publishing, 1974.

Pollution Probe Foundation. *Think Before You Spray: Alternatives to Chemical Pesticides*. Toronto, 1983.

Society Promoting Environmental Conservation. *Pest or Guest*. Vancouver, 1985.

Yepsen, Roger B., Jr., ed. *The Encyclopedia of Natural Insect & Disease Control*. Emmaus, Pennsylvania: Rodale Press, 1984.

Booklets

Non-Toxic Lawn Care. Available from Canadian Organic Growers (see list of groups above for address).

Seed Sources for Organic Gardeners. Available from Canadian Organic Growers (see list of groups above for address).

Magazines

COGnition, Canadian Organic Growers. P.O. Box 6408, Station J, Ottawa, Ontario K2A 3Y6. Quarterly.

Harrowsmith. Telemedia Publishing Inc., 7 Queen Victoria Road, Camden East, Ontario K0K 1J0; (613) 378-6661. Six issues a year.

Organic Gardening. Available from P.O. Box 7000, Georgetown, Ontario L7G 9Z9. Monthly.

The Prairie Garden. Available from Winnipeg Horticultural Society, P.O. Box 517, Winnipeg, Manitoba R3C 2J3. Annual.

Products

Organic Fertilizers and Pesticides
Canagro Agricultural Products Ltd.
Box 130
Elmira, Ontario N3B 3A2
(519) 669-1586

Fossil Flower
6860 Century Avenue
Mississauga, Ontario L5N 2W5
(416) 821-4430

Manchester Fertilizer
87 Ainslie Street South
Cambridge, Ontario N1R 3K8
(519) 621-5910

Purity Life
100 Elgin Street South
Acton, Ontario L7J 2W1
(519) 853-3511

Safer's Ltd.
465 Milner Avenue
Scarborough, Ontario M1B 2K4
(416) 291-8150

Beneficial Insects for Biological Pest Control
Applied Bio-Nomics Ltd.
8801 East Saanich Road
Sidney, British Columbia V8L 1H3
(604) 656-2123

Better Yield Insects
P.O. Box 3451
Tecumseh Station
Windsor, Ontario N8N 3C4
(519) 727-6108

Fossil Flower
6860 Century Avenue
Mississauga, Ontario L5N 2W5
(416) 821-4430

Index

Polystyrene Packaging Council, 68
Port Coquitlam, 25
Potts, Chief Gary, 106
Power plants, 7, 14
Prairie Conservation Action Plan, 119
*Preventing Petroleum Storage Tank
    Leaks: A Citizen's Guide*, 54
Prince Edward Island, 16, 47, 71, 91,
    96
Priority Substances List, 79
Probe Post, 41, 50, 77, 79, 85
Probe International, 63, 64
*Problems Facing Canadian Farmers
    Using Organic Agricultural
    Methods*, 102
*Protecting Life on Earth: Steps to
    Save the Ozone Layer*, 40
*Protecting Ontario's Natural
    Heritage through Private
    Stewardship*, 119
*Protecting the Ozone Layer: What
    You Can Do*, 40
Provigo, 38
Public Citizen, 147
Public transportation, 18, 30, 172,
    178-80
Purity Life, 184
Pyrethrum, 133, 186

Quebec, 7, 9, 11, 14, 16, 18, 28, 44,
    50, 88, 91, 93, 96, 107-8, 111
Quebec City, 43
Quotations from Chairman Zalm, 114

Radon, 162, 164-65
*Radon Reduction Methods: A
    Homeowner's Guide*, 165
Rainforest Action Network, 59, 63
Rainforest Action Week, 64
Rainforests, 57-64
    causes of deforestation, 58-61
    definition, 58
    distribution, 59
    effects, 61-63
    extent of deforestation, 61

government, 61
solutions, 63-64
temperate rainforest, 117
Ramsay, Jennifer, 182
Rawson Academy of Aquatic Science,
    55
Reagan, Ronald, 14
Recycling, 73, 75, 136-37
    "Blue Box," 71, 75, 136-37
    CFCs, 39, 40
    hazardous waste, 134
    motor oil, 70, 75, 175
    paper, 70, 75
    reducing air pollution, 18, 73
    reducing energy used, 18, 70, 73,
        136
    symbol, 73
Recycling Council of Ontario, 139
Recycling Week, 75
Refrigerators, 34, 38, 39, 148, 149-50
Reid, Ron, 52
Reilly, William, 17
Remedial Action Plans, 50, 53
Renner, Michael, 172
Reptile Breeding Foundation, 121
Road salt, 12, 47, 48
Robinson, Alan, 67
Rocky Mountain Institute, 153, 173
Rokeach, I., & Sons, 131
Rotenone, 186
Rowland, Sherwood, 33
Royal Society of Canada, 46
R2000, 159
Rust primer, 132
Ryley, 143

Safer Inc., 133, 184, 186
St Lawrence National Institute of
    Ecotoxicology, 121
St Lawrence River, 43-44, 45, 46, 50,
    121
Salvation Army, 74, 140
Saskatchewan, 10, 91, 96, 120
Saskatchewan Environmental
    Society, 74

Saskatchewan Natural History
    Society, 118
Saskatchewan Wildlife Federation, 118
*Saving Energy and Money with
    Home Appliances*, 154
Schiff, Harold, 33
Science Council of Canada, 46, 48,
    49, 55, 92, 95, 96, 97, 101
*Sensitivity of Western and Northern
    Canada Surface Waters to
    Acidic Inputs*, 10
Sewage, 43-45, 47, 52, 73, 127, 135
Shaklee Canada, 131
Shea, Cynthia Pollock, 40
Sierra Club of Western Canada, 118
Simon, Mary, 84
Smith, Ron, 3
Smoke detectors, 135
Soap Factory, 131
Soap Works, 131
Société pour vaincre la pollution, 52,
    87
Society for Preservation of Wild
    Culture, 53-54
Soil at Risk, 89, 90
Sol, 147
Solar Energy Society of Canada, 147
Solomon, Lawrence, 38, 169
Solvents, 35, 44, 132
Species extinction, 3, 27, 57, 58, 61,
    109-10, 118, 121
Speirs, Rosemary, 114
Spider plants, 163
Sprayers of Dioxin Association, 101
Standing Senate Committee on
    Agriculture, Fisheries and
    Forestry, 90
State of the Environment Report,
    97, 115
State of the World 1989, 21, 25, 27,
    28, 35
*Status of Wildlife Habitat in
    Canada*, 110, 111
Stopping Acid Rain, 15, 16
Stove, 149, 150, 151-52, 162

We All Need the Earth . . . Now the Earth Needs You!

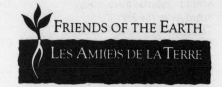

One in three Canadians now considers the environment *the* most pressing issue in the country. We know that you are concerned, since you have picked up this book.

BUT WE DON'T HAVE THE LUXURY OF TIME. The earth, our life support system, is threatened.

FRIENDS OF THE EARTH NEEDS YOUR HELP TO PROTECT THE PLANET

Friends of the Earth is the largest network of environmental groups in the world, with offices in 36 countries and half a million members worldwide. Friends of the Earth is able to press for international action and we have a 20-year record of campaigning for positive change.

Since 1978, Friends of the Earth Canada has been on the leading edge of environmental activism, campaigning for solutions to critical problems that face the planet today.

We have made a lasting difference with campaigns to protect the ozone layer, stop air pollution that causes the "greenhouse effect," ban the toxic herbicide Alachlor, teach students about tropical rainforests, ban leaded gasoline and promote energy conservation. We are also helping homeowners stop using chemicals on their lawns with our book, *How to Get Your Lawn and Garden Off Drugs*, and are continuing the struggle to have PCBs in Canada treated properly.

We place a high priority on answering those "what can I do" letters and calls by providing useful environmental tips on everyday activities like housecleaning and travelling to work.

THE 1990S: YOUR CHANCE TO ACT

Years of abuse have left their mark on the face of the earth. Many scientists fear that the earth cannot take one more decade of destruction.

The 1990s offer a window of opportunity for change. The message for us is loud and clear. Action today is crucial if we are to give our children the option of enjoying the planet tomorrow.

WHAT KEEPS US GOING?

First and foremost, your support. Contributions from individuals make our advocacy, research and education campaigns possible. Your membership helps make our pro-environment voice impossible to ignore.

Environmental problems are complex. But the solutions can be as simple and as far-reaching as changing a light bulb, or riding a bike. By joining us you can become part of the solution. Become part of a team working to protect the earth for tomorrow.

Cut along dotted line and send to us today.

PLEDGE YOUR SUPPORT FOR THE EARTH TODAY . . . JOIN FRIENDS OF THE EARTH

The earth needs friends now more than ever. You can make a difference.

Friends of the Earth members receive *EarthWords*, our quarterly newsletter, regular campaign updates, fact sheets and flyers, and a prompt response to your questions.

Yes, I'm a friend of the earth! I enclose:

☐ $100   ☐ $50   ☐ $35
☐ $25   ☐ Other $ _____

☐ Charge $ _____ to my VISA/MasterCard

Card # _____

Expiry Date: _____

Signature: _____

☐ Please send a receipt for tax purposes. The first $10, which covers membership services, is not tax-deductible.

Name: _____

Street: _____

City: _____

Prov.: _____ Code: _____

Telephone: (____)_____

Send to:
Friends of the Earth
701-251 Laurier Ave. W.
Ottawa, Ontario K1P 5J6
(613) 230-3352

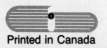

Printed in Canada